AUTOCAL WORKBOOK

PHIL METHERELL

Lecturer, Plymouth College of Further Education

Edward Arnold
A division of Hodder & Stoughton
LONDON NEW YORK MELBOURNE AUCKLAND

© 1989 P G Metherell

First published in Great Britain 1989

Distributed in the USA by Routledge, Chapman and Hall, Inc.
29 West 35th Street, New York, NY 10001

British Library Cataloguing in Publication Data

Metherell, Phil
  Autocad workbook.
  1. Microcomputer systems. Software packages:
  Autocad
  I. Title
  005.36'9

  ISBN 0–340–51371–3

Printed and bound in Great Britain for Edward Arnold, the
educational, academic and medical publishing division of Hodder
and Stoughton Limited, 41 Bedford Square, London WC1B 3DQ by
Butler & Tanner Ltd, Frome and London.

INTRODUCTION TO THE AUTOCAD WORKBOOK

This workbook is designed to help new users to learn the basics of AutoCad. It is not necessary to have previous computer experience but a little knowledge of Personal Computers and their operating system, MS-DOS, would be useful. The text does not aim to be a comprehensive explanation of all AutoCad's many commands but gives guidance on most of the commonly used functions in an effort to give you an understanding of the way in which the program operates so that eventually you will be able to respond to a previously unknown command in the correct way.

At present, the only national qualification in CAD is offered by the City and Guilds of London Institute (Computer Aided Draughting and Design Using AutoCad ; Number 4351) and the WorkBook has been prepared with the syllabus for this exam in mind.

All the examples and exercises use metric units although AutoCad is quite capable of using Imperial units if desired.

Do not despair if things do not seem to be working out as every new user has been tempted to throw the computer through a window at some stage. Learning AutoCad can be likened to learning to ride a bike, you fall off a couple of times to start with but once you have grasped the basics then you will be up and away and wondering what all the fuss was about.

WHY USE CAD ?

The initials CAD can be defined as Computer Aided DRAUGHTING or Computer Aided DESIGN , the distinction is a fine one, but it is generally accepted that the DESIGN definition includes functions other than straightforward DRAUGHTING. For example, some packages will carry out structural calculations, or simulate the performance of a printed circuit design. Most of the Design types of software are expensive and require expensive equipment to run them.

AutoCad is principally a DRAUGHTING package, but many firms offer software that works with AutoCad, turning it into a DESIGN tool. One of the main reasons that AutoCad has become almost an industry standard is that it runs on relatively inexpensive Personal Computers yet it manages to retain most of the facilities normally associated with systems costing ten times as much. This allows many small firms and individuals to benefit from the use of CAD systems at an affordable price.

The drawing takes place on a screen and the CAD software provides commands for making this process as convenient and accurate as possible. these commands can be seen as being analagous to the traditional draughtsman's tools of set square, compass, "Letraset" and so on. In order to be as powerful and as adaptable as AutoCad is, it appears to be complicated to use but this is not necessarily true. It is quite possible to produce drawings at an early stage once the basics of the program have been mastered and the techniques can be refined as you get to know the program better.

Some of the benefits of using CAD as opposed to conventional methods are :-

a) SPEED -

> Many claims have been made concerning this aspect but it very much depends on the applications. A drawing that contains much repetition or shows arrangements of standard components benefits most and can be up to 4 or 5 times as fast as drawing board methods. A complex drawing of a "one-off" nature may not benefit at all.

b) ACCURACY -

> There can be no dispute that CAD systems are potentially much more accurate than drawing by hand. If a line is to be 3491mm long then this is exactly the length the program stores and will scale it extremely accurately when plotted thus avoiding the need for scale rules and the estimating they require. Of course the output is only as precise as the input and the old adage "Garbage in, garbage out" applies.

c) CONVENIENCE -

> There are many respects in which a digitised drawing is more convenient to use. These include the ease of amendment, the ability to plot to any scale, the use of colour, semi-automatic dimensioning, the storing of drawings in a very compact and accessible form and many more.

d) PRESENTATION -

> As well as producing images on screens for discussion, CAD generated drawings on paper have a clean, crisp appearance and if amendments are needed then this is done on the computer and a new plot produced with no blemishes that are typical of a drawing negative modified by hand. Although some critics find CAD drawings "mechanistic", it is easy to produce a "house style" to your own tastes. This can then be consistent across all your drawings.

e) FURTHER USES -

> In the mechanical and electrical engineering fields, the use of Computer Aided Manufacture is ever increasing, where the digital drawing files control the machines that produce the item. Information of a non-graphical nature can be entered into the drawing eg product code, price, colour etc, to be later extracted to form a Bill of Materials. There are also drawing management systems which will log the time each drawing is being worked on and other information useful for costing the design process.

Software vendors make much of their products abilities to design in 3 dimensions. A true 3-D system is often called a "solid modeller" and once the model has been input will automatically generate desired elevations, sections etc. Any changes to the original model will automatically update the views. These systems are not very "friendly" to use and are expensive. Other systems, of which AutoCad is one, offer a 3-D visualisation facility where a model can be produced which is useful at the concept stage but it is usual that production drawings are carried out in 2-D. Some systems offer only 2-D draughting.

The text for the AutoCad WorkBook was prepared on Wordstar, the diagrams on AutoCad and the resulting files processed through Ventura Publisher by the author who would like to thank the College of Further Education Plymouth for their cooperation.

AUTOCAD is the Registered Trademark of Autodesk Inc.

CONTENTS

INTRODUCTION TO THE AUTOCAD WORKBOOK   *i*

0 : AUTOCAD SOFTWARE AND HARDWARE   *0/1*

1 : LOADING AUTOCAD AND STARTING A DRAWING   *1/1*

2 : DRAWING AND ERASING LINES, CIRCLES AND ARCS,
DISPLAY CONTROL   *2/1*

3 : SETTING UP THE DRAWING ENVIRONMENT,
DRAWING AIDS   *3/1*

(REFERENCE SHEET FOR FUNCTION KEYS)   *3/8*

ASSIGNMENTS 1, 2, 3

4 : FURTHER DRAWING AND EDITING, POLYLINES   *4/1*

5 : ENTERING TEXT, TEXT STYLES, MORE EDITING   *5/1*

6 : LAYERS, LINETYPE AND COLOUR   *6/1*

ASSIGNMENTS 4, 5, 6

7 : CREATING AND USING BLOCKS   *7/1*

8 : HATCHING, EXTRACTING INFORMATION AND
MORE EDITING   *8/1*

9 : DIMENSIONING DRAWINGS   *9/1*

10 : 3-D VISUALISATION   *10/1*

ASSIGNMENTS 7, 8, 9

11 : PLOTTING A DRAWING   *11/1*

APPENDIX A: MS-DOS AND INSTALLING AUTOCAD   *A/1*

APPENDIX B - RELEASE 9   *B/1*

INDEX

0 : AUTOCAD SOFTWARE & HARDWARE

AutoCad first appeared in the USA in 1982 and quickly gained a reputation as a flexible and relatively "friendly" CAD program. Because of its success,as with all popular types of software, it is improved and extended at intervals and the various (later) versions are listed below :-

a) Version 2.05 - 2D draughting

b) Version 2.18 - 2D draughting + 3D visualisation

c) Version 2.5 - Enhanced draughting features + Autolisp

d) Version 2.6 - Faster and further enhanced version of 2.5.

e) Release 9 - Current version with new menu display and 3D enhancements.

f) Release 10 - Soon to be available and this is the last Version to be run under MS DOS. Its main enhancement is an extended 3D facility.

As a general rule, drawings created in earlier versions of AutoCad will load into later versions but the reverse is not possible.

In fact one of AutoCad's strengths is that it is upwardly compatible, which means that commands and techniques in earlier versions will still work in later versions so avoiding a re-learning with each release.

AutoCad also market an Educational Version of the program which is identical to the full version but it will not save or plot drawings. This Educational version is only £50 but if you are using this, some of the exercises in this book which require saving information will not work.

Versions later than 2.18 require a hardware lock or "dongle" to be installed in the back of the computer in order to run. This is an anti-piracy device. Release 9 (& the future Release 10) require an additional chip to be present in the computer called a maths co-processor. This speeds up the calculations involved and was previously an optional extra but is now obligatory.

HARDWARE FOR AUTOCAD

COMPUTERS

AutoCad runs on the IBM PC family of computers and this includes the IBM PC XT, the IBM PC AT, the IBM PS/2 range and most clones of these machines. A minimum specification of 640Kb internal RAM and a Hard Disk (often 20 Mb capacity) is necessary to run AutoCad. A working system can be based around a machine such as the Amstrad PC1640 at about £1000 and a typical top line system would use a computer based on the Intel 80386 chip with extended memory of 2Mb and a fast 40 or 60 Mb hard disk e.g. IBM PS/2 Model 80 costing up to £5000. AutoCad can also be run on some minicomputers which use a different operating system.

PERIPHERALS

DISPLAY

The IBM PC series offers a number of options for display devices suitable for AutoCad and the resolution of these is quoted as the number of pixels across and down the screen. A pixel is one dot on the screen and the whole picture is composed of a large number of these dots, the more dots in a given screen size, the higher the resolution. Starting with the least desirable, the most common options are :-

a) Colour Graphics Adaptor (CGA) + Colour monitor - This will give a choice of 8 colours, only four of which are on-screen at any time, with poor resolution (320x200 pixels).

b) Hercules Mono Graphics Adaptor + Mono monitor - This is a monochrome display but with higher resolution than the CGA (720x348 pixels).

c) Enhanced Graphics Adaptor (EGA) + Colour Monitor - 16 colours and medium resolution (640x350 pixels).

d) Professional Graphics Adaptor (PGA) + Special Colour Monitor - 256 colours and High resolution (640x480 pixels).

e) Video Graphics Array (VGA) + Multisync Monitor - 15 colours and High Resolution (640x480 pixels)

f) Specialist systems e.g. Cambridge Graphics - Usually a very high resolution graphics screen (typically 1024x768 pixels) used in conjunction with a separate text screen .

INPUT DEVICES

In addition to the normal computer keyboard, one or more of the following devices can be used with Auto-Cad :-

a) Mouse - either the roller ball or the optical type of mouse to control position on screen and to select commands from a screen menu.

b) Digitiser - In addition to controlling position on screen, this device will select commands from the screen menu and a "tablet" menu placed on the pad. It can also be used to digitise existing paper drawings for use in AutoCad.

c) Lightpens, trackerball, joystick etc - although much less common than a) and b), some types of these devices can be used.

STORAGE DEVICES

Drawings as digital information can be stored on floppy discs, mostly 5.25 inch discs at present but likely to be 3.5 inch in future. Even within these sizes, there are options :-

a) 5.25 Double Density formatted to hold 360 Kb as on the IBM PC XT.

b) 5.25 Quad Density formatted to hold 1.2 Mb as on the IBM PC AT.

c) 3.5 formatted to hold either 720 Kb or 1.44 Mb as on IBM PS/2 range.

Just for comparison purposes a typical architectural drawing occupies about 200 kB.

The most convenient storage for current drawings is on the hard disc and for old or archive drawings a tape streamer is often used. To avoid the consequences of Sod's Law, it is essential to keep back-up copies on floppy disc even of current drawings.

In larger offices that can afford and justify the hardware, recently, it has become possible to store drawings on CD disks.

OUTPUT DEVICES

For quick but crude copies of drawings, a dot- matrix printer can be used but for proper drawings, a plotter is essential. These are mostly pen-plotters at present in which the computer controls the movement and selection of pens which are moved over the paper. They come in a variety of sizes from A3 (at about £800) to A0 (£5,000 to £15,000). Electrostatic plotters are available which produce copies quickly but the machines are very expensive and laser printers can produce good resolution at A4 size.

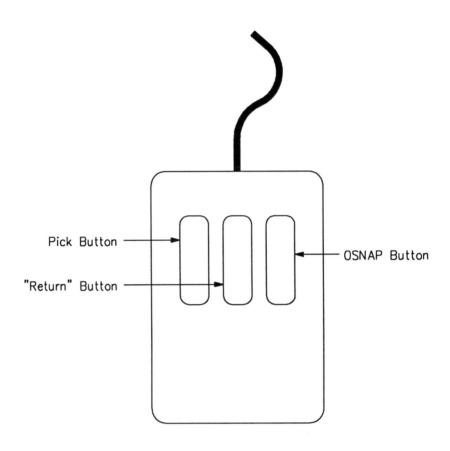

Pick Button

"Return" Button

OSNAP Button

Fig. 0/1 - The Mouse

NOTES

THE MOUSE

The mouse can be a rollerball type which runs on the desktop or an optical mouse which runs on a reflective pad. Whichever type, it has a dual function in the draughting process.

Function 1 - It controls the position of the "CURSOR" on the drawing area. The cursor can be likened to the tip of the pen or pencil in conventional draughting and is shown as the intersection of the horizontal and vertical lines on the screen. If you run out space on the reflective mouse pad then simply pick up the mouse and replace on the pad at a different location.

Function 2 - It is used to highlight and select the commands in the menu area.

Mice can have two or three buttons and these are dedicated to different uses. A three button mouse will have the functions listed below :-

LEFT BUTTON - The "pick" button which is used to fix a point on the drawing screen e.g. start of a line and this button selects a command which has been highlighted in the menu area.

MIDDLE BUTTON - This duplicates the "Return" key of the keyboard. One frequent use of this is to repeat a command as hitting the "Return" key will repeat the most recently used command. For example, to draw a series of unconnected lines by repeated use of the LINE command without having to select it each time from the menu.

RIGHT BUTTON - Pressing this button will cause the OSNAP menu to appear together with a few other commands e.g. REDRAW. This would be used mainly in conjunction with drawing commands. For example, if you select the LINE command and you want the first point of the line to connect with an existing feature of the drawing then you would use the right button to give access to the OSNAP modes from which the appropriate choice can be made.

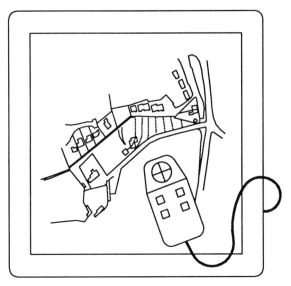

Fig. 0/2 - Digitiser with Existing Drawing

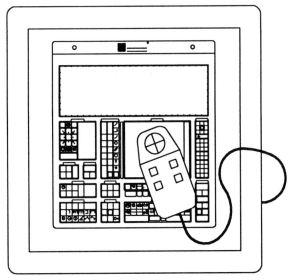

Fig. 0/3 - Digitiser with Tablet Overlay

NOTES

THE DIGITISER

A digitising tablet can be used not only to select commands and to fix points on the screen in a similar manner to the mouse but can also be used to digitise existing drawings. After fixing a drawing down on the bed of the digitiser, the various drawing features can be "picked" by the digitiser puck and eventually the paper drawing will be digitised into the computer as an AutoCad drawing. This process has to be treated with a little caution however as the orginal may not be accurate, the paper may have stretched or shrunk and there is a limit to the accuracy with which points on a drawing can be picked with the puck. This technique is especially useful for, say, maps but in many cases can require so much editing that it would be quicker to re-draw it directly into the computer.

When used in conjunction with the AutoCad tablet overlay, the main advantage of a digitiser compared to a mouse is that you do not have to go through the hierarchical structure of the screen menu. For example, to draw a line with the mouse, you first have to select DRAW then LINE from the screen menu whereas the LINE command is immediately available from the overlay. The digitiser with tablet overlay has three main functions :-

Function 1 - Commands can be selected off the overlay by placing the crosshairs of the puck over the command and pressing the "Pick" button.

Function 2 - When the crosshairs are in the screen pointing area of the overlay, this will fix positions on the drawing screen.

Function 3 - The strip down the right edge of the screen pointing area controls the normal screen menu in just the same way as a mouse.

The puck can have different arrangements of buttons but four is a common type, in which case their functions are normally :-

Button 1 - is the "pick" button for selecting commands and points on screen.

Button 2 - is a duplicate of the "Return" key.

Button 3 - gives access to the OSNAP modes.

Button 4 - is the "Cancel" button and will halt any command.

You may be using a digitiser in conjunction with a stylus instead of the puck in which case, pressing the point down is the equivalent of the "pick" button and pressing the point on a grey area of the overlay is the same as pressing "Return".

Module Title	No.	Date Completed	Student Initials
AutoCad Software	0		
Loading AutoCad	1		
Drawing & Erasing	2		
Drawing Aids	3		
Assignment	01		
Assignment	02		
Assignment	03		
Polylines	4		
Text	5		
Layers	6		
Assignment	04		
Assignment	05		
Assignment	06		
Blocks	7		
Extracting Info.	8		
Dimensioning	9		
3D Draughting	10		
Plotting a Drawing	11		
Assignment	07		
Assignment	08		
Assignment	09		

Fig. 0/4 - Module Progress Chart

ADVICE ON USING THE AUTOCAD WORKBOOK

1) If you have not yet installed AutoCad on your computer, then you should consult Appendix A which also gives some guidance on MS DOS.

2) The WorkBook is arranged as a series of modules indicated by the page number eg 4/6 is Module 4, Page 6. Although it is sensible to work through them in order, after completing the first three modules, you can choose them in any order. If you have some familiarity with the program then you might be able to "speed-read" or skip some sections.

3) There is an area provided with each module for you to make your own notes on the module content and exercises. This is a valuable method of reinforcing the topic and could be useful when you actually use AutoCad in a working environment.

4) The exercises are loosely structured and you will seldom be directed as to the precise key presses to make. You will make mistakes, but when this occurs, see if you can understand why, as this can be very instructive .

5) At three points in the book, you will find assignments which are possible to complete with the knowledge learned from the preceding modules. You should be able to carry out these assignments before proceeding.

6) The "Return" key is used frequently and one of the main uses is to "finish" an item typed in from the keyboard. Wherever you come across the word "Enter" in the text, this means type something in and press "Return".

7) Even though Release 9 is the current version of AutoCad at the time of writing, the WorkBook is written to conform to Version 2.6 as it was felt that the extra expense of adding a maths co- processor as required by Release 9 would inhibit the use of this later version especially in educational institutions. You will notice little difference in operation and Appendix B covers the differences between Version 2.6 and Release 9.

8) It is assumed throughout that you will be using a mouse and will generally be selecting commands from the screen menu. Where there is a significant difference between this approach and, say, using a tablet menu on a digitiser, the tablet menu option will be shown in *Italic typeface*.

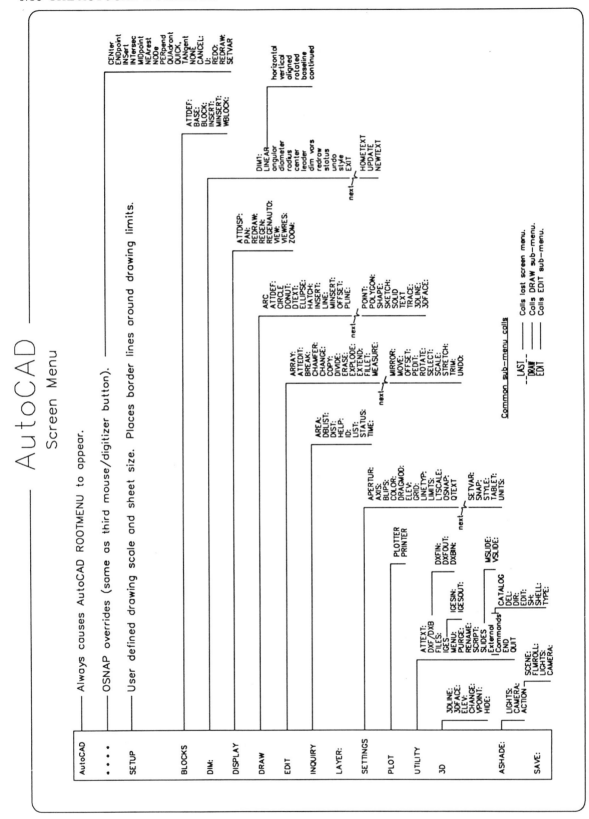

Fig. 0/5 - Screen Menu Layout

1 : LOADING AUTOCAD and STARTING A DRAWING

PRE-REQUISITE KNOWLEDGE

You should have a working version of AutoCad and should know how to use the keyboard and how to use the mouse. You should also be reasonably familiar with the manual production of technical drawings.

OBJECTIVES

After completing this module you should be able to:

1) Load AutoCad into the computer.

2) Understand the options of the opening menu.

3) Start a new drawing.

4) Know the functions of the AutoCad screen.

5) Appreciate the use of the Rootmenu.

6) Use the AutoCad "Help" facility.

INTRODUCTION

In this first module, you will be introduced to the procedure for loading AutoCad and how to commence a drawing. The way that AutoCad uses the VDU screen will be explained and you will learn how to select commands. You will learn how to use the AutoCad on-screen "HELP" facility to augment these notes.

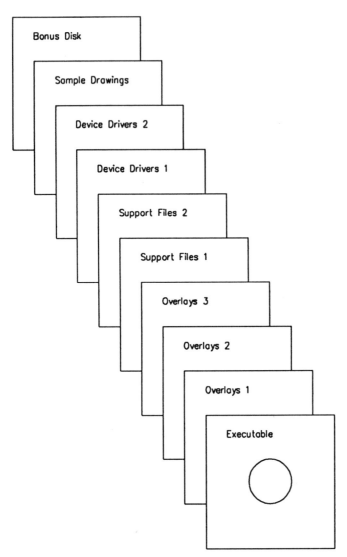

Fig. 1/1 - AutoCad Program Disks

NOTES

LOADING AUTOCAD

It is assumed that you have AutoCad installed on your computer in a directory called "AUTOC". If Auto-Cad is not yet installed, consult Appendix A. If the directory is called something else then just replace "AUTOC" in the instructions below with your directory name.

When you switch the computer on, it will test its memory then load MS DOS and when you see the prompt

C>

it is waiting for you to start.

First log on to the directory which contains AutoCad (CD is shorthand for Change Directory)

1) Enter   CD AUTOC

Next load the program

2) Enter   ACAD

Hints & Tips

1) If it does not cause to much confusion at this stage, you could have entered the following at the C> prompt, prior to loading AutoCad :-

SET LISPHEAP=15000

SET LISPSTACK=10000

This reserves some memory to allow you to run some special commands at a later stage. (see SETUP)

2) Most users create a Batch file which is a list of the necessary commands to load AutoCad but this re-quires some knowledge of DOS and a text editor.

3) Several menu systems exist for hard disks which will simply allow you to choose AutoCad from a list displayed on screen.

AUTOCAD

Copyright (C) 1982,83,84,85,86,87 Autodesk, Inc.

Version 2.6j (5/12/87) IBM PC

Advanced Drafting Extensions 3

Serial Number: 94-301100

Main Menu

0. Exit AutoCAD

1. Begin a NEW drawing

2. Edit an EXISTING drawing

3. Plot a drawing

4. Printer Plot a drawing

5. Configure AutoCAD

6. File Utilities

7. Compile shape/font description file

8. Convert old drawing file

Enter selection:

Fig. 1/2 - AutoCad's Main Menu

NOTES

THE MAIN MENU

When AutoCad has been loaded, the opening menu will be displayed as shown in the Screen Details panel:-Most of these options are self-explanatory but some clarification might be useful.

Options 1 or 2 : you will be asked for a drawing name which can be up to 8 characters long and may include numerals as well as letters.

Options 3 & 4 : allow you to produce a paper copy of the drawing either on a pen plotter or, for quick but crude copy, on a dot matrix printer.

Option 5 : is chosen when AutoCad is loaded for the first time or if a change has been made to the hardware running the program. It tells AutoCad which devices it has to run.

Option 6 : allows the user to list files, copy files, erase files etc.

Option 7 : may be ignored as this is a very specialist area.

Option 8 : is used to load drawings created on very old versions of AutoCad.

Exercise

Select *Option 1* - Start a NEW drawing and give it a name of your choice. After a short delay, the Auto-Cad Graphics screen will appear.

Hints & Tips

1) If you are familiar with DOS, the name may be preceded with a drive and/or directory specification, e.g. A:\PLANS\HOUSE4 will refer to Drive A, Directory called PLANS and a drawing HOUSE4. Do not try to use the normal MS DOS three letter file extension as AutoCad supplies this. A drawing file is saved with the extension .DWG.

2) When you have created many drawings, you will appreciate the importance of using a convention for naming drawings. My own system is of the form :-

4 letters which are shorthand for the project name

2 numerals for the drawing number, starting with 01

1 letter for indicating revisions

e.g. LLEA03B would be for a project called Linden LEA, drawing number 03 and revision B.

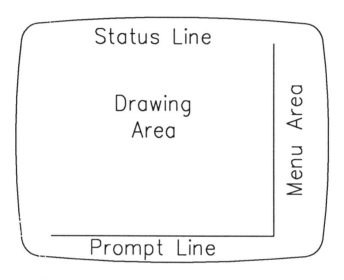

Fig. 1/3 - The Graphics Screen

NOTES

THE GRAPHICS SCREEN

The screen has four main areas as shown in the Screen Details panel.

The **STATUS** line displays information about various settings that the user can specify including drawing aids (see later module).

The **MENU** area shows the **ROOTMENU** of the AutoCad drawing editor and will show further menus selected by the user.

The **PROMPT** line will display the word *"Command . '* when it is waiting for a command to be entered. This is the area where you will be prompted for information required by the commands. Alongside the prompt AutoCad often gives a "default" value which is either the last value you used or is set by Auto-Cad. If you wish to accept this default value, simply press "Return" otherwise enter the new value.

The **DRAWING** area is where the drawing will be displayed.

If you are using a single monitor, the screen you are viewing is the GRAPHICS screen but AutoCad supports a TEXT screen which can be switched on by pressing the function key F1. This key operates as a toggle switch between the two screens. In normal use the text screen shows you one "screen- full" of the commands you have entered. Some AutoCad commands automatically switch you to the text screen e.g. HELP.

If you are using a setup that has two monitors then one will always be the Graphics screen and the other will be the Text screen.

Exercise

Enter the command HELP and then press "Return" as the prompt suggests. The display will switch to the text screen and show you a list of all the AutoCad commands. Use F1 to return to the graphics screen.Now enter HELP again but this time enter a command name e.g. LINE at the prompt.

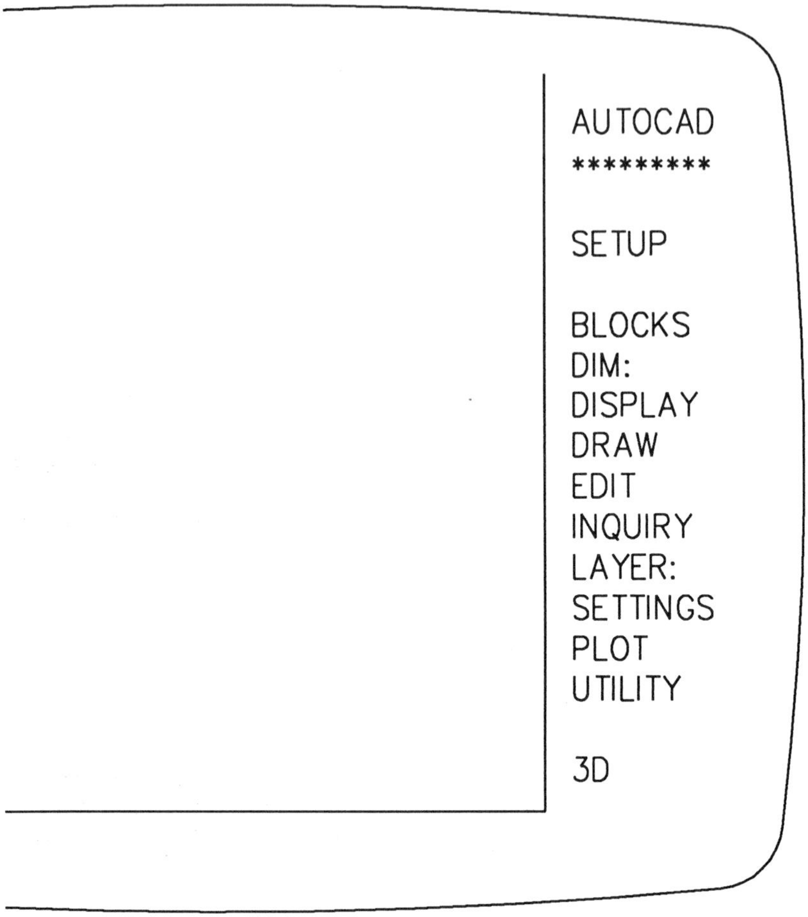

AUTOCAD
****

SETUP

BLOCKS
DIM:
DISPLAY
DRAW
EDIT
INQUIRY
LAYER:
SETTINGS
PLOT
UTILITY

3D

Fig. 1/4 - The Rootmenu

NOTES

THE ROOTMENU

AutoCad has a menu system that is based on the "tree" structure (actually it is more like the roots of a tree than its branches) and the "rootmenu" gives a series of broad headings under which lie the Auto-Cad commands which, in turn, give access to further commands and sub-commands . A diagram of the menu structure is included in MODULE 0.

Wherever you are in the menu structure you can get back to the rootmenu by selecting the word "AUTOCAD" at the top of the menu area.

Selecting the row of stars below AUTOCAD gives access to the OSNAP modes. The use of this feature will be explained in a later module.

The heading "SETUP" is a special command for specifying paper size etc. and you should avoid it at this stage.

Exercise

Select each of headings in the Rootmenu using the mouse and examine the commands that it gives access to. Return to the Rootmenu by selecting "AUTOCAD" at the top of the screen. Note that any rootmenu heading covers a group of commands that are associated e.g. DRAW covers lines, circles, arcs etc . Also you will see that when you have, for instance, selected DISPLAY, at the bottom of the screen menu will be the headings DRAW,EDIT and LAST. These can be selected to give access to their underlying commands without having to go back to the Rootmenu.

If you are using a digitiser, you can carry out the above exercise but also examine the tablet overlay, and you will find that the commands are grouped together in a very similar manner to the Rootmenu headings.

TWO POINTS TO REMEMBER

1) You cannot damage the equipment by pressing keys or buttons and if you you get "caught" in a command, pressing "Ctrl" and "C" together will stop the process and return to the "Command :" prompt. *There is the command "CANCEL" on the tablet overlay.*

2) There is a help facility on AutoCad which can be accessed at the "Command :" prompt . To view the help, type in the command "HELP" or simply "?" and then respond to the next prompt with the name of the troublesome command.

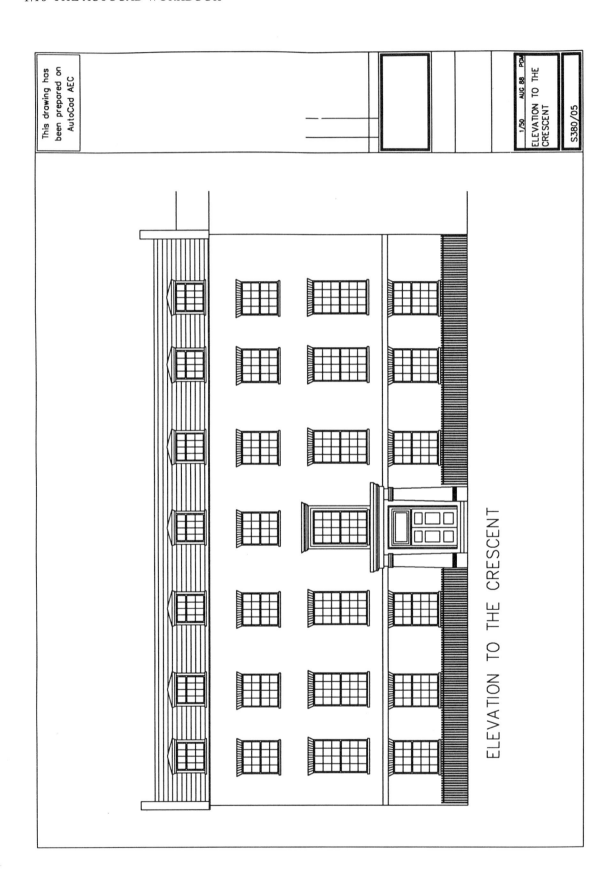

This drawing has been prepared on AutoCad AEC

1/50   AUG 88   PO4

ELEVATION TO THE CRESCENT

S380/05

ELEVATION TO THE CRESCENT

2 : DRAWING AND ERASING LINES, CIRCLES AND ARCS , DISPLAY CONTROL

PRE-REQUISITE KNOWLEDGE

In order to derive maximum benefit from this module, you should be able to load AutoCad, to use the mouse or digitiser and to start a new drawing.

OBJECTIVES

After completing this module you should be able to:

1) Define a point on the drawing screen.

2) Draw lines.

3) Erase lines.

4) Draw circles and arcs.

5) Use ZOOM to control the screen display.

6) Save and Quit from a drawing.

INTRODUCTION

In this module you will be introduced to some of the most frequently used AutoCad commands but even more importantly, you will learn the style in which AutoCad expects you to enter information. Many of the options which are used with these few commands are also found with a large number of other commands that you will meet in later modules.

You might find that some examples appear clumsy to execute but there are often quicker ways of carrying them out when you have mastered more features of the program.

Even though it may not seem important at this stage, a thorough understanding of the ways in which to input information will be a great asset in later work.

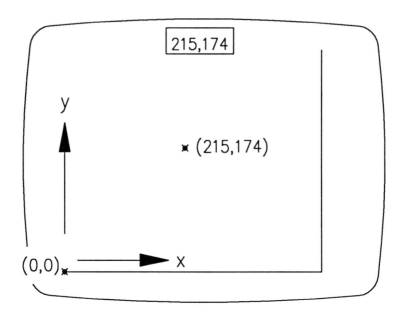

Fig. 2/1 - X,Y Coordinates

NOTES

DEFINING POINTS

An essential part of the draughting process is to fix points on the screen as ends of lines, positions to enter text etc and AutoCad provides a number of ways of doing this. When you have become more familiar with the program you will use a combination of these methods to produce a drawing.

Before trying any of these methods, it should be clarified that the drawing area is set up like a piece of graph paper with the "x" axis along the horizontal and the "y" axis running vertically. The "origin" i.e. (0,0) is conventionally in the bottom left corner and any point on the screen can be defined in terms of its x and y coordinates.

Exercise

Move the cursor on the screen with the mouse and note the changing coordinates displayed on the status line at the top of the screen. If this does not seem to respond, press the function key, F6 as this is the key which determines whether the coordinate display is activated. Note the coordinates of the top right corner.

We shall see later that the "size" of the drawing area can be set to any value that you wish.

Defining a point

Method 1) Using the mouse to position the cursor by eye, possibly in conjunction with the coordinate display.

Method 2) Using the mouse in conjunction with SNAP (see later)

Method 3) Typing in the coordinates from the keyboard in the form **x,y** . Note the comma !

Exercise

Select DRAW then LINE from the menu and draw some lines, defining their endpoints using both the methods 1) and 3). Note that once selected, you will remain in the LINE command enabling you to draw a series of connected lines, until you press "Return" (either on the keyboard or on the mouse) to halt the LINE command .

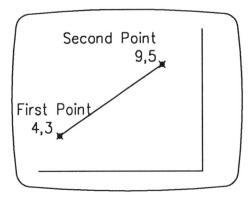

Fig. 2/2 - Absolute Coordinates

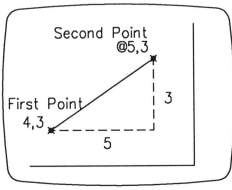

Fig. 2/3 - Relative Coordinates

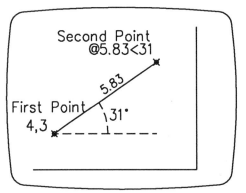

Fig. 2/4 - Polar Coordinates

NOTES

DEFINING FURTHER POINTS

The AutoCad LINE command requires both a start and finish point to be defined. These can be defined in just the way you used in the previous exercise.However there are alternative ways of defining the second point relative to the first point rather than from the (0,0) origin.

> Method 1) Specifying the x and y increment to get from the first point to the second point. This is achieved by entering the increments in x and y from the keyboard in the form

> **@ x increment , y increment**

> e.g. @5,3 would place the second point 5 from the first in the x direction and 3 in the y direction.

> Method 2) Use polar coordinates to specify a distance and angle from the first point. You should note that angles are usually measured anticlockwise with zero lying due east. The form is

> **@distance<angle**

> e.g. **@5.83<31**   would fix the same point as Method 1.

When the coordinate display is active, you will notice that after the First Point has been fixed, the display changes to give the distance and angle of the present cursor position relative to the defined First Point.

Exercise

> Select DRAW then LINE and experiment with using all the options for drawing a series of connected lines.

To produce a closed figure if you type "c" in response to the "To Point :" prompt, a line will be drawn to your original starting point.

If you make a mistake in fixing a point then the UNDO facility can be used to "un-fix" the last point.

Exercise

> Draw several connected lines then before exiting the LINE command, enter U in response to the "To Point" prompt and note the effect. By repeatedly entering U the lines will be removed right back to (and including) the first point.

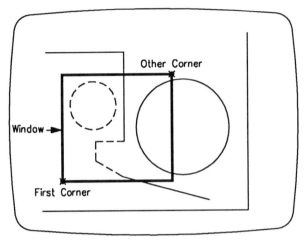

Fig. 2/5 - Erasing by Window

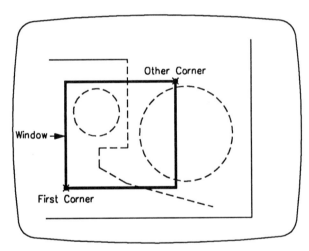

Fig. 2/6 - Erasing by Crossing

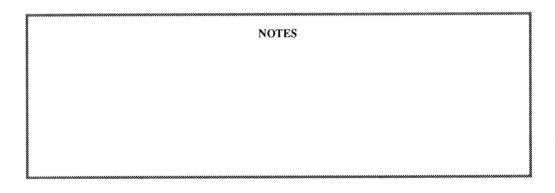

NOTES

ERASING LINES

The **ERASE** command will remove any unwanted lines from a drawing and its use at this time will also introduce some general principles concerned with editing drawings.

With virtually all **EDIT** commands, you will be prompted at some stage to define the object you wish to edit and this can be done in several different ways. Which ever method is used , the objects that Auto-Cad thinks you have specified will be shown "ghosted" and you will have to press "Return" to confirm the selection. You can decline by entering "Ctrl" & "c".

The various object selection techniques are as follows :-

> **"point"** - Use the mouse to position the target box over the object. This is the default mode i.e. the method which is expected when the command is selected. All the other modes require them to be specified before selecting objects.

> **L -** Edit the last object drawn.

> **W -** Construct a window around objects by defining bottom left corner of window and dragging the rectangular window to the required size and then pressing the left button. Only objects that are totally within a window will be selected. The concept of a window is a common feature of Auto-Cad and is also extensively used in changing the screen display.

> **C -** Similar to the window option but in this case any objects that cross through the window will be selected.

> **A** - Add more objects to those already selected.

> **R -** Remove objects from those already selected.

> **U -** Undo the most recent selection.

These options can be specified by selecting from the screen menu or by typing in the first letter (e.g. W for Window) or directly from the tablet overlay.

After erasing objects, you will be left with "blips" on the screen. To remove these, use the REDRAW command, which can be found at the bottom of the OSNAP menu activated by the right mouse button.

Exercise

Select EDIT then ERASE. Use a variety of options to select lines from your previous exercise to remove. Watch carefully to see how AutoCad interprets your selection.

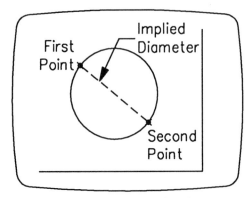

Fig. 2/7 - 2-Point Circle

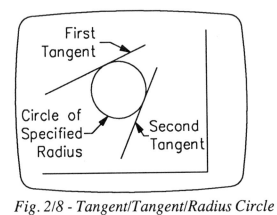

Fig. 2/8 - Tangent/Tangent/Radius Circle

Fig. 2/9 - Terminology of Arcs

NOTES

DRAWING CIRCLES AND ARCS

Now that you have learned to draw straight lines, the drawing of circles and arcs should be reasonably straightforward. Any difficulty might arise from the number of ways of defining these features. AutoCad provides a variety of ways of defining both circles and arcs and the choice of any particular method will depend on the circumstances.

Exercise

Select DRAW then CIRCLE. To start, choose the Centre/Radius option. After you have fixed the centre point on the screen you will then be prompted to enter the radius but AutoCad also gives the "DRAG" option. Move the mouse to see the effect of this. Try some of the other options.

The ARC command gives an even greater range of options and you should use the HELP facility to obtain details of the options.

Exercise

Draw some arcs using different options and note that the arc is drawn anti-clockwise so the order in which you specify the start and finish points is significant.

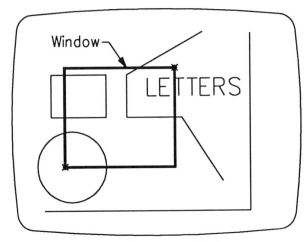

Fig. 2/10 - Zoom,Window

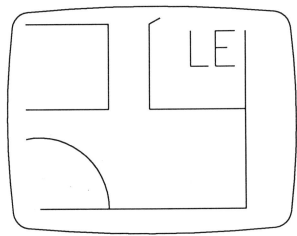

Fig. 2/11 - Display after Zoom

NOTES

DISPLAY CONTROL

Up to now you have been drawing on the whole drawing area but you will have appreciated that in order to draw small details or accurately locate features, it would be desirable to magnify parts of the screen. This is accomplished by using the ZOOM command.

Once again there are several methods of specifying the type of zoom and you should consult the HELP file for precise definitions. One of the most useful options is the "window". Like the window used by the ERASE command, you will be asked to declare a window on the drawing and the features within this window will then be magnified to fill the screen. Using ZOOM and "all" will return the whole drawing to the screen.

Exercise

Select DISPLAY then ZOOM then "window" to magnify an area of your drawing. Note that you can use the same options to further magnify an area of the "zoomed" drawing. Use other options to discover their effect.

The ZOOM "dynamic" option is very useful for moving from one area of a drawing to another and the Window can be re-sized during the process.

Exercise

Use ZOOM "dynamic" to alter the display and pay particular attention to the selection of mouse buttons necessary to complete the process. The pick button is used to alter the window size and the "Return" button to actually cause the zoom to take place. A certain amount of trial and error may be necessary.

Hints & Tips

1) ZOOMing a complex drawing can be very time consuming, not that the effect is apparent from a single zoom, but during a draughting session you will zoom many times so the cumulative effect may be significant. The ZOOM , Dynamic option can avoid the time-wasting regeneration of the image by providing an hourglass icon in the corner of the screen. If this is displayed the a complete regeneration will occur , if however you manipulate your proposed viewing window you can often cause the icon to disappear in which case a much faster ZOOM will result.

SAVING AND QUITTING A DRAWING

Before attempting the next module, you should know how to leave the present drawing. It is unlikely in this instance that you would wish to SAVE your present drawing, but should you like to practice the   procedure :-

Exercise

Select UTILITIES then SAVE: your drawing name declared at the start will be given as the default and you should press "Return" to confirm this or you can enter a new name. The hard disk should be activated and the drawing saved.

This process has not dropped you out of the drawing yet :-

Exercise

Select UTILITIES then QUIT: you will be asked if you really want to do this because if the drawing has not been previously saved then this is your last chance to back out before it disappears. Enter YES (or simply Y) and you will be returned to the opening menu.

Hints & Tips

1) There is an END command which performs the function of the SAVE and QUIT commands in one go, but if you use this then the size of the drawing files created will be much larger than the method described above. Typically four times larger ! This is because the END command also saves the sequence of commands used to create the drawing in case at some later date you should wish to use the UNDO command repeatedly to undo work done in the present session.

NOTES

3 : SETTING UP THE DRAWING ENVIRONMENT,

DRAWING AIDS

PRE-REQUISITE KNOWLEDGE

In order to derive maximum benefit from this module, you should be able to load AutoCad , to use the menu system and to draw and erase lines.

OBJECTIVES

After completing this module you should be able to:

1) Appreciate the concept of a drawing environment.

2) Set relevant drawing sizes.

3) Set relevant drawing units.

4) Set and use drawing aids.

5) Devise and use a prototype drawing.

INTRODUCTION

In order to speed up the drafting process and to give greater convenience, it is useful to be able to set up various features of AutoCad. The program is extremely open to customisation for use in a particular application and this module provides the first steps in the process.

Using the correct settings and drawing aids is essential if you are to realise the full benefits of speed and accuracy offered by AutoCad.

The commands you will meet are LIMITS, UNITS, GRID, SNAP, ORTHO and the various OSNAP modes.

SETUP

The AutoCad Rootmenu has an option called SETUP, but this is not a real AutoCad command in the same sense as the LINE or ZOOM commands. It is a short sub-routine written in AutoLisp which is a programming language supplied with AutoCad. For this reason it will not work if sufficient memory has not been reserved for it. This has to be done before loading AutoCad and the necessary commands are given in Module 1.

Assuming that you have set aside enough memory, then the routine works like this :-
> 1) You are asked what type of units you will be working in :-

> a) Decimal e.g. 34.98 or 1679.5

> b) Scientific e.g. 3.498E+01 or 1.6795E+03

> c) Imperial e.g. 4'-7 1/4"

> 2) Once you have selected a unit type you will be asked to define what one drawing unit represents. For example, when the coordinate display shows 4, does this mean 4 Metres or 4 Millimetres.

> 3) Next you will be asked what scale you intend to plot the drawing at.

> 4) Finally you will be required to state the paper size that you intend to plot on.

Once this information has been fed in then the SETUP routine works out how big the drawing area should be and draws a border around it. It also sets various parameters to relevant values.

When you start drawing you enter all lengths in full size units as the final PLOT routine will take care of the scale.

Exercise

> Start a new drawing and use the SETUP command to specify that you will be using decimal units, that one drawing unit is to be a millimetre, that you intend to plot at 1:50 on an A1 sheet.

When the routine has finished the prompt line tells you that you have a drawing area that is 42050 x 29700mm. This would be suitable for an architectural drawing of the floor plan of a large building for instance.

The next few pages of this module explain how to set the various parameters manually as it is important to understand exactly what is going on.

Hints & Tips

One reason why I tend to be wary of the SETUP command is that it assumes that you will be able to plot the full A size sheet. In practice, drum plotters have rubber rollers that grip the long edges of the paper sheet and you cannot plot on the strip occupied by the rollers. The end effect of this is that if you are using true A size sheets then there will be about a 10mm strip down each long edge that cannot be used. Thus a true A1 sheet of 841x594mm has an effective size of about 841x570mm and any drawing near the long edges e.g. the border, will not be plotted. This can be overcome by using over-size plotting sheets e.g. 841x615mm if you can get them or by manually setting the limits to 841x570.

SETTING UP THE DRAWING ENVIRONMENT

If you do not use the SETUP option, you can set all the parameters to suit your own drawing style and whch are consistent with your plotters mode of operation. It is essential in the long term that you understand this process as it is an integral part of AutoCad's operation.

The input of data to form a drawing is independent of the scale at which the drawing will later be plotted and a decision on this scale need only be made prior to plotting. If all drawings are prepared using full size dimensions then the coordinates of the drawing area of the screen when fully ZOOMed must be large enough to accept these dimensions.

For example : if an object which is 280mm long by 150mm high is to be drawn then, if the bottom left corner is (0,0), the top right corner would conveniently be set at (400,250). This would allow room for the drawing plus a margin around it.

LIMITS

The command that implements this is LIMITS. When the command is called, you will be prompted for the coordinates of the bottom left and top right of the screen and you should enter the relevant numbers. The screen will only display the area set by LIMITS if you do a ZOOM, All afterwards.

Exercise

Select SETTINGS then LIMITS. Now input the appropriate data for the drawings described below :

i) A map which covers an area of 1400m x 800m

ii) An electrical component 6mm x 6mm

iii) A piece of furniture 1000mm x 350mm

(You can see if your answers approximate to those given at the end of this module.)

Hints & Tips

1) As the proportions of the drawing area are about 3:2 , it is sensible to use these ratios for your specification of limits, otherwise you will be only working in a part of the available area.

2) Drawing objects outside the limits is possible but can have unpredictable effects. You can re-specify your limits at any time to include previously unforseen objects.

3) You could specify the bottom left corner to be "negative" e.g. (-30,-20) so that the the corner of the actual drawing was located at (0,0). This can avoid considerable mental arithmetic.

SETTING UP THE DRAWING ENVIRONMENT

UNITS

AutoCad allows five different types of linear units to be used with varying degrees of displayed accuracy. You can also specify angles in five different ways with a choice of orientation of zero.

Exercise

Select SETTINGS then UNITS. If you hit "Return" at each prompt you will see the options possible (with examples) but will not actually change anything.

Exercise

Set the appropriate units for a drawing of an object which is 4m x 3m but contains details measured to the nearest millimetre. Angles will be decimal degrees to 4 decimal places and zero is "North". Try drawing some lines using keyboard entry to test whether you are correct.

SETTING UP THE DRAWING ENVIRONMENT

GRID

A featureless drawing screen is somewhat intimidating and AutoCad provides a facility to display a grid of dots at intervals specified by the user.

To initially set the grid spacing, either type in the command GRID or select it from the SETTINGS menu. Respond to the prompt with the desired spacing and the grid will appear to fill the whole drawing area set by the LIMITS command.

The grid can be turned off (and back on) at any time with the function key F7. (Other function keys also control other drawing aids which we will meet in this module and included at the end of the module is a reference sheet on this.)

Exercise

Use GRID to set a spacing for the drawing described in the previous exercise. Then turn it off, then on.

SNAP

The SNAP command is used to "lock" the cursor on to a specified grid and no points off this grid can be selected with the mouse while SNAP is active. This is a particularly useful feature where a drawing is based on, say, a 25mm module with all dimensions being multiples of 25. With the SNAP set at 25 then the cursor will only move to points whose coordinates are multiples of 25 e.g. (50,75) , (2350,975) etc.

The grid used by SNAP can be the same as the visible GRID but does not have to be so. Indeed it is more usual, for instance, to set GRID to 500 and SNAP to 100.

SNAP is turned on/off by the F9 key.

Exercise

Set a suitable SNAP for the proposed drawing and see the effect of this. Change the spacing and observe the difference.

Hints & Tips

1) The grid does not have to be square but can be rectangular by selecting to define a new aspect ratio. An isometric grid is also available.

2) It can be confusing if the visible GRID is not a multiple of the SNAP grid e.g. in the above example, a SNAP setting of 75 would not be recommended.

3) Use a piece of removable sticky tape placed on the keyboard beside the function keys to note down their use.

SETTING UP THE DRAWING ENVIRONMENT

ORTHO

As many drawings are composed mainly of horizontal and vertical lines, AutoCad provides an ORTHO command which only permits lines to be drawn in these directions. This is purely an on/off function controlled by the F8 key and does not require any other setting.

Exercise

Draw some lines with ORTHO on and pay particular attention to the coordinate display of the status line. This gives a distance and angle.

PROTOTYPE DRAWINGS

You might find that you have to produce a number of similar drawings for which the drawing environment will be the same. In this case it is tedious to have to set them all for each drawing.

A more efficient solution is to set all the desired features then save the blank drawing with a drawing name such as PROTO1.

If you then want to start a new drawing which you will call "NEWDWG" then the procedure is :-

    1) At the opening menu, choose Option 1: Start a new drawing

    2) Specify your drawing name as

NEWDWG=PROTO1

The drawing will now have the default name of NEWDWG but will have all the settings of PROTO1.

You could set up a number of these "prototype" drawings with your commonly used environments and then select the appropriate PROTOx at the start.

Hints & Tips

1) Prototype drawings can also have a blank title block, standard notes, your own preferred style of text and many other features pre-defined which can greatly speed up the draughting process.

DRAWING AIDS - OSNAP

There are many occasions when you want to join a new drawing element on to a specific feature of a drawing. If this point happens to coincide with your SNAP grid then there is no problem but this is not the usual situation. Object SNAP (OSNAP) provides an immediate solution to many of these occurences. The command is "transparent" which means that it can be issued within most drawing and editing commands without stopping the command running. Because it is so frequently used, it is made available by either pressing the right mouse button or by selecting the row of stars at the top of all screen menus.

OSNAP will lock the cursor on to a variety of features of a drawing. You should consult "Help" for a complete listing but we will consider two commonly used options, namely, ENDpoint and INTersection. The ENDpoint option locks the cursor on to the end of an existing line and the INTersection option locks the cursor on to the point where two lines cross or form a corner.

The sequence of use is :-

      a) Select the appropriate draw or edit command.

      b) In response to the prompt "First Point" select OSNAP by either of the methods described above.

      c) Select the relevant OSNAP mode.

      d) Position the target box over the feature on the drawing and fix it. This will be the "First Point".

      e) Repeat for any subsequent points.

Exercise

Draw a rectangle then form a "Union Jack" effect making maximum use of OSNAP. Next join some arcs to the outsides of the rectangle.

Hints & Tips

1) The size of the target box can be adjusted by using the APERTURE command.

2) If you want to use one particular OSNAP mode repeatedly then this can be set before selecting a drawing or editing command by entering "OSNAP" then typing in the desired mode. Abbreviations such as INT for INTersection are allowed. After use the mode can be switched off by entering "OSNAP" then "NONE".

Answers to LIMITS exercise

i) 1600,1000

ii) 8,8 (or 12,8)

iii) 1200,500

REFERENCE SHEET FOR FUNCTION KEYS

All the function keys operate like on/off switches and change the parameters listed below :-

F1 - Switches between the text and the graphics screen. Some commands automatically send you to the text screen e.g. "STATUS" and to return to the drawing screen press F1. Using F1 to switch from the drawing screen to the text screen during drafting will display a screenful of all the commands and prompts used most recently which can be useful if you want to refresh your memory.

F2 to **F5** are non-operational.

F6 - turns the COORDINATE display at the top of the screen on/off.

F7 - turns the screen GRID on/off

F8 - selects/de-selects the ORTHO function for drawing only horizontal and vertical lines.

F9 - turns the SNAP function on/off

F10 - *applies only to digitiser users and it switches the mode between digitising existing drawings and its use with the tablet overlay. "Tablet on" means it is in the digitising mode.*

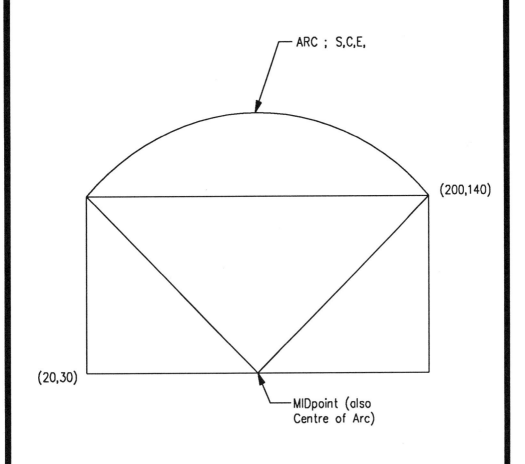

ARC ; S,C,E,

(200,140)

(20,30)

MIDpoint (also
Centre of Arc)

SETTINGS INFORMATION :

LIMITS – 0,0 & 300,200
GRID – 20
SNAP – 10 (when required)
ORTHO – as required

DRAWING ASSIGNMENT No : 01
DATE COMPLETED : _____
STUDENT INITIALS : _____
THE AUTOCAD WORKBOOK

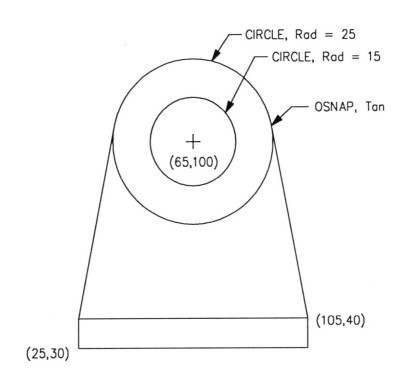

CIRCLE, Rad = 25

CIRCLE, Rad = 15

OSNAP, Tan

(65,100)

(105,40)

(25,30)

SETTINGS INFORMATION :

LIMITS – 0,0 & 200,150
GRID – 10
SNAP – 5
ORTHO – ON for Baseplate

DRAWING ASSIGNMENT No : 02
DATE COMPLETED : _____
STUDENT INITIALS : _____

THE AUTOCAD WORKBOOK

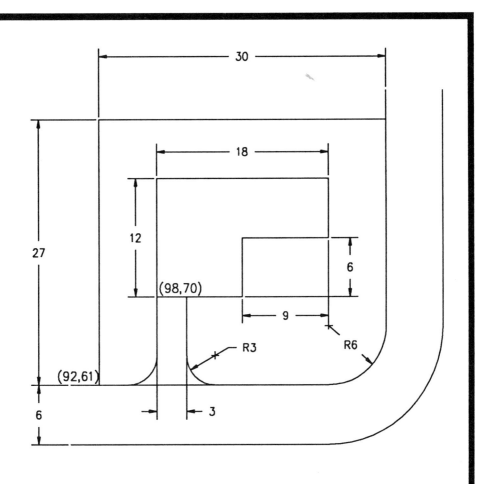

SETTINGS INFORMATION :

LIMITS – 80,50 & 140,120
GRID – 5
SNAP – 1
ORTHO – ON

DRAWING ASSIGNMENT No : 03
DATE COMPLETED : _____
STUDENT INITIALS : _____

THE AUTOCAD WORKBOOK

4 : FURTHER DRAWING AND EDITING, POLYLINES

PRE-REQUISITE KNOWLEDGE

In order to derive maximum benefit from this module, you should be able to start a drawing, set up a drawing environment and use some drawing and editing commands.

OBJECTIVES

After completing this module you should be able to;

    1) Draw ellipses, polygons and doughnuts.

    2) Draw simple polylines.

    3) Use the editing commands BREAK, OFFSET, TRIM & FILLET.

INTRODUCTION

You have already learned how to draw lines, circles & arcs and how to erase them. AutoCad provides many more drawing commands to facilitate the drawing of more complex objects. You will also appreciate that the ERASE command only removes whole objects, however you will often need to remove parts of objects and to modify existing objects in a variety of ways. In this module we will investigate some more editing commands.

As you have learned how to specify points when drawing and how to select objects for editing, the style in which these further drawing and editing commands are used should be familiar.

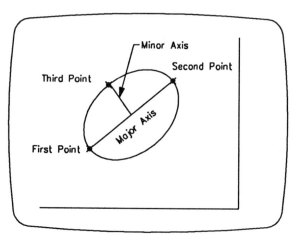

Fig. 4/1 - Ellipse

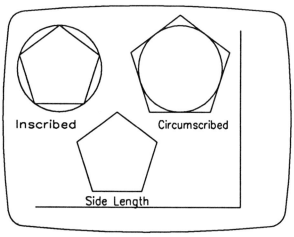

Fig. 4/2 - Polygons

NOTES

DRAWING ELLIPSES

Any drawing which contains a circle viewed from anywhere but "head-on" will require the construction of an ellipse. In isometric drawing, ellipses are a common feature and AutoCad provides a special option of the ELLIPSE command to do this.

The AutoCad ELLIPSE command has four methods of defining an ellipse but at this stage we will only examine one of these. This option expects you to define a line which is one axis of the ellipse (usually the major axis but not necessarily so) then to specify half the length of the other axis.

Exercise

Select DRAW then ELLIPSE. In response to the first prompt, fix a point which will be one end of an axis then fix the other end in response to the second prompt. You now indicate the half-length of the other axis. Watch the screen as you do so.Draw some more ellipses especially noting AutoCad's response to the fixing of the third point.

DRAWING POLYGONS

This command allows you to draw any regular polygon. You can have any number of sides from 3 to 1024. The size of the polygon can be specified by :-

i) The radius of the circle within which the polygon is drawn i.e. Inscribed.

ii) The radius of the circle which fits within the polygon i.e. Circumscribed.

iii) The length of one edge of the polygon.

On selecting the polygon command the sequence of prompts is in the following order :-

a) Number of sides ?

b) Centre of the polygon ? (or edge length ?)

c) Inscribed or Circumscribed ?

d) Radius of circle ?

Exercise

Draw a number of polygons by any of the three methods.

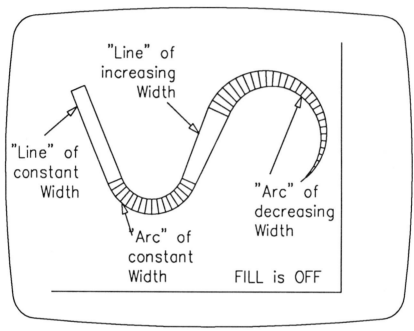

Fig. 4/3 - Polylines

NOTES

DRAWING POLYLINES

Polylines are a special AutoCad feature which enables you to draw a series of interconnected lines and/or arcs. A further option allows you to specify widths (in drawing units) for these lines or arcs. After you have drawn a series of lines/arcs, AutoCad then treats the combination as a single object so, for example, the ERASE command will remove the entire polyline. A special polyline edit command, PEDIT, is provided to allow editing of parts of a polyline. One interesting facility of the PEDIT command will fit a smooth curve to a series of lines/arcs that comprise a polyline. This could be particularly useful for operations like plotting contours.

The PLINE i.e. **PolyLINE** command works in the following sequence :-

a) You are prompted to define the start point of the polyline.

b) Then you are asked for the endpoint of the present section of polyline or given a series of options for:

    i) choosing an arc.

    ii) closing a polyline back to the startpoint.

    iii) specifying the length of the next portion.

    iv) undoing the most recently drawn portion.

    v) defining the start and finish width of the present portion.

    vi) defining the half-width at the start and finish of the present portion.

NB some of these options do not make sense when you have just started a polyline e.g. Close or Undo.

c) The prompt will then be repeated to allow you to add further portions of polyline, or for example, change widths, until it is complete when pressing "Return" will finish the command.

Exercise

Select DRAW then PLINE. Fix the start point on the screen, then enter "W" to define a width. Type in a starting width which is sensible bearing in mind the "scale" of your drawing. Enter a finishing width then fix the endpoint. Next select "A" (for Arc) and then fix the endpoint of the arc. Carry on defining new portions with different widths etc until you are confident about the command. When you press "Return"to finish the polyline, notice how AutoCad removes it then redraws it. This process makes it a single object (rather than the series of objects you defined).

Hints & Tips

1) When drawing polyline arcs, make sure ORTHO is off or you can get some unexpected results.

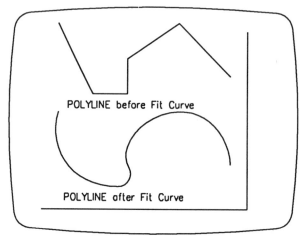

POLYLINE before Fit Curve

POLYLINE after Fit Curve

Fig. 4/4 - Pedit - Fit Curve

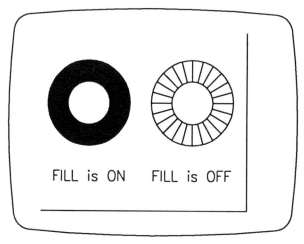

FILL is ON   FILL is OFF

Fig. 4/5 - Doughnuts (or Donuts)

NOTES

PEDIT

The PEDIT command will not be explored fully here but the next exercise demonstrates its "Fit curve" option.

Exercise

Start a new polyline and build it up from a series of straight lines of width zero. When you have several lines drawn, finish the PLINE command. Select EDIT then PEDIT, select your polyline and then the "Fit curve" option. Watch the screen.Try this again with polylines of a specified width.

Polylines may not seem all that useful at this stage but as you get to know AutoCad better, you will find that it is a very powerful function. In fact the ellipses, polygons and donuts you are drawing are all specialised forms of polyline.

DRAWING DOUGHNUTS

A Doughnut (or DONUT) is two circles with the same centre point but different radii. The space between the two circles is filled in (if the FILL option is ON).

You are simply asked for the radii of the two circles then the centre point of the donut.

Exercise

Draw several donuts. Note that AutoCad remembers the radii of the previous donut and will use these values as its default, so facilitating the drawing of several donuts of the same size.

Hints & Tips

1) To draw a completely filled circle, draw a DONUT with an internal radius of zero.

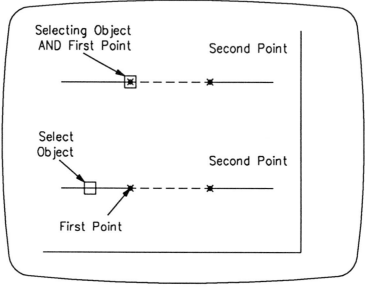

Fig. 4/6 - Break

EDITING DRAWINGS

The only EDIT command you have encountered so far is the ERASE command but there are a large number of other commands for changing a drawing.

BREAK

The BREAK command will erase parts of an object (unlike the ERASE command which removes entire objects).

When this command is chosen (as with most Edit commands) you will first be asked to select the object to be broken. In this instance, the precise point at which you select the object can be one end of the section to be removed. In this case, the next prompt will result in you defining the other end of the section to be erased. The section will then be shown "ghosted" for your approval . Pressing "Return" will erase the marked section.

If it is not convenient to choose the object and the "First Point" at one attempt then you may simply select the object at any point on it. Next reply to the prompt " Second Point " by typing "f", you will then be asked for the precise location of the start of the break.

If you are using the tablet overlay then you will notice that there are two variations of the BREAK command available to you namely BREAK F and BREAK @ . BREAK F automatically supplies the "f" for "First Point" as described above and BREAK @ simply breaks an object into two without removing a portion.

Exercise

Draw some LINEs and then use BREAK to remove parts of them. Next draw some circles and arcs and BREAK them. Note which portions of circles are removed and their relationship to the way in which you defined "First" and "Second" Points.

Exercise

For tablet overlay users, draw a number of lines and use BREAK F and BREAK @. You will notice that BREAK @ causes a single line to become two contiguous lines. If you try to ERASE a line treated in this way, you will see the effect.

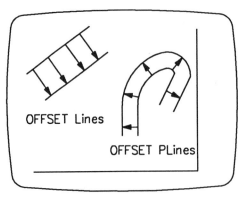

OFFSET Lines

OFFSET PLines

Fig. 4/7 - Offset

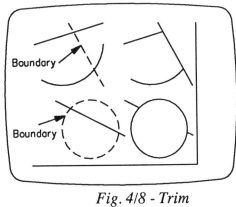

Boundary

Boundary

Fig. 4/8 - Trim

Original Lines   after FILLET=0

Original Lines   after FILLET radius=8

Fig. 4/9 - Fillet

NOTES

MORE EDITING

OFFSET

The OFFSET command draws a parallel line to an existing line (and polyline) and is extremely useful. You have to specify the existing line, the offset distance and which side of the original line you wish the new line to appear.If you enter "T" for "Through" when prompted for the offset distance, then you can offset an object so that it runs through a desired point on the drawing.

FILLET

The FILLET command inserts a fillet radius between two existing lines but one of its main uses is its use with a fillet radius of zero. This option will "neaten" a corner with two overlapping lines or will extend two non-intersecting lines to form a corner.

On the tablet overlay, there are two versions of the FILLET command , FILLET 0 always has the fillet radius set to zero and FILLET will accept a radius defined by you.

TRIM

If you want to remove the sections of lines that extend beyond a certain boundary, the TRIM command will accomplish this. With this command you have to declare the line that forms the boundary first, then all the objects that you want trimmed at that boundary. If you select two boundaries and have an object that crosses both, then the section between the boundaries will be removed when it is selected as the object to trim.

Exercise

Draw some lines and arcs and practise the use of these commands. Draw a closed polyline then use OFFSET and note the way in which AutoCad interprets this.

Hints & Tips

1) If you want to draw "concentric" rectangles, then it is more efficient to draw the original rectangle as a polyline and offset this than to draw the rectangle as four lines, to offset each of these lines then to neaten up each of the four corners. If having the rectangles as polylines creates problems later, they can be changed back into lines with the EXPLODE command.

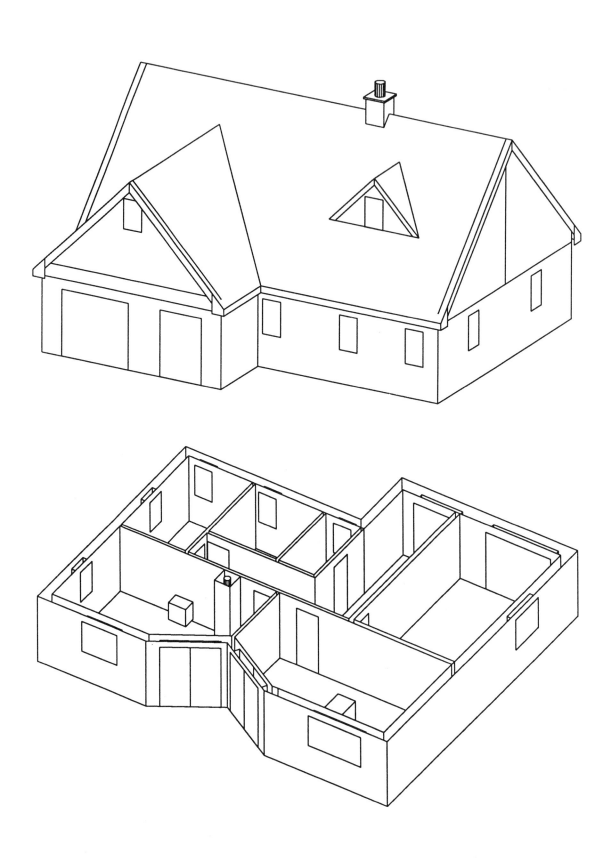

5 : ENTERING TEXT, TEXT STYLES, MORE EDITING

PRE-REQUISITE KNOWLEDGE

In order to derive maximum benefit from this module, you should have be able to use some AutoCad drawing commands.

OBJECTIVES

After completing this module you will be able to :-

1) Enter text on to a drawing.

2) Use Dynamic text insertion.

3) Modify existing fonts to create your own text style.

4) Use the edit commands MOVE, COPY, MIRROR, ROTATE & CHANGE.

INTRODUCTION

All drawings will contain some text items , if only the title, and AutoCad provides a convenient way of doing this. Labelling and titling drawings can be a fairly lengthy process when carried out manually and any errors that arise can be difficult to amend. An added benefit is that the appearance of the text will be consistent throughout a drawing or series of drawings.

Text used in dimensions will not be covered here as it is a subject in its own right.

AutoCad provides two modes for text entry. There is the older TEXT command in which text only appears on the drawing screen at the end of an entry and there is the more recent Dynamic TEXT (DTEXT) which places the text on screen as it is typed in and allows simple editing at this stage.

The final section of this module introduces some more commands for editing objects and text.

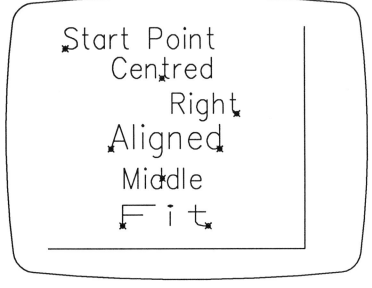

Fig. 5/1 - Text Alignment

NOTES

POSITIONING TEXT

We will investigate the DTEXT command as in most respects, it is more convenient than the TEXT command.

AutoCad provides several methods of positioning text on the drawing. These are listed below :-

Start Point - prints text to the right of the designated point which is the bottom left corner of the first character.

Center - spaces text evenly about the specified centre point of the baseline.

Right - Places right end of text against specified point.

Aligned - spaces the text between two points you indicate. AutoCad supplies a suitable height for the text.

Middle - Like "Center" but text height is centred about specified point as well as text length.

Fit - Like "Aligned" but height is fixed by you.

With all but Aligned text you will be prompted for the height (in drawing units) for the text. AutoCad remembers the last height you used and uses this as a default value for your consideration.

The command sequence is :-

a) Select DTEXT (under DRAW).

b) Enter the desired positioning mode, (START POINT is the default so if this is the mode you want then just fix the Start Point).

c) Enter position(s) for all modes other than START POINT.

d) Enter Height.

e) Enter Rotation angle (Zero for horizontal text)

f) A box will appear at the specified position and the box is of the correct size to enclose a character at the height you have specified. Enter the text.

On pressing "Return" at the end of an entry the text box moves to the next line down for another entry if desired. This will continue for as many lines as you wish to enter. To finish off an entry, press "Return" with the box having just moved to a new line.

Exercise

Use the DTEXT command and all of the positioning modes to place text on the screen.

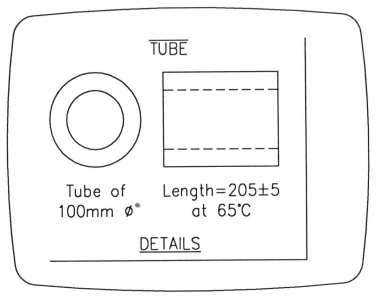

Fig. 5/2 - Special Text Characters

NOTES

SPECIAL CHARACTERS

There is a way of placing some special characters in your text. The codes given below should be typed in full in the normal text way to display the desired character. Two of the codes do not produce characters but draw a line either above or below the following text and the code acts like a on/off switch. Type it once at the start of the section to turn it on and again at the end to turn it off.

%%c - circle diameter symbol, the Greek letter "phi".

%%d - the degrees symbol.

%%p - the plus/minus symbol for tolerances.

%%% - the percent symbol.

%%u - turns the underscore on/off.

%%o - turns the overscore on/off.

Exercise

Try copying the diagram on the facing page

TEXT COMMAND

With the DTEXT command, the text is inserted on the screen as you type and permits you to use the backspace key to remove errors. With the TEXT command nothing appears on the screen until you have finished typing in the text. Also TEXT does not allow repeated lines of text without re-selecting TEXT between successive lines. Probably the TEXT command was retained to maintain compatibility with older versions which did not have the DTEXT command, as DTEXT is much more convenient.

Hints & Tips

1) It is as well to pay attention to your final plotting scale when specifying a text height or else it may be unreadable. For example, if you want text which is 4mm high at a scale of 1:50, then the height will be 200 on screen.

2) Centred text will appear to the right of the specified centre point as it is being typed in because AutoCad has no way of knowing how long the entry will be. When you finish the entry, it will be centred. Multiple lines will be centred beneath one another.

3) Text can slow down regeneration of a drawing (after a ZOOM for instance) so there is Quick TEXT (QTEXT) mode which displays text as a box of appropriate size in the correct position.

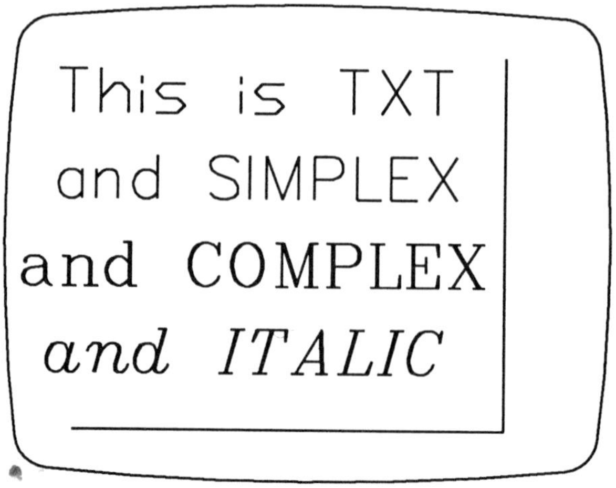

This is TXT
and SIMPLEX
and COMPLEX
and ITALIC

Fig. 5/3 - Font Files

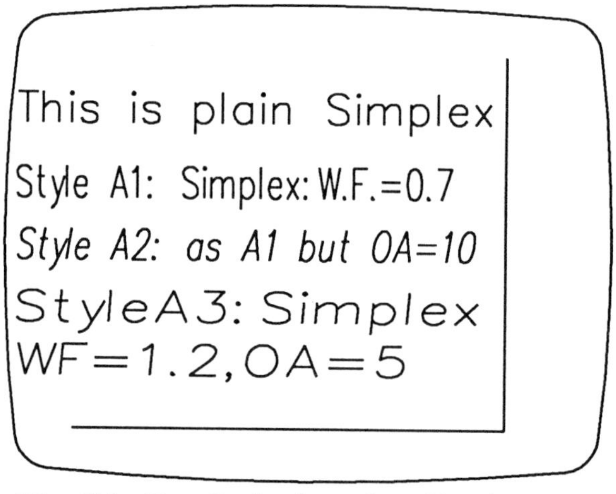

This is plain Simplex
Style A1: Simplex: W.F.=0.7
Style A2: as A1 but OA=10
StyleA3: Simplex
WF=1.2,OA=5

Fig. 5/4 - Text Styles based on Simplex Font

NOTES

TEXT STYLES

The style of lettering you have been using is that which AutoCad automatically loads at the start. This is only one possible style. AutoCad comes with four basic font files (many more in Release 9). You can manipulate any of these to provide variations of your choice.

The basic fonts are :-

    a) Txt

    b) Simplex

    c) Complex

    d) Italic

Any of these FONTS can be altered to give a STYLE and the style you have been using is called "Standard" and is based on the "Txt" font.

To create your own style, you use the STYLE command. This is not to be confused with the "style" option of the DTEXT command, which is discussed below.

When the STYLE command has been selected, you will be asked for a name of your choice (you should avoid using any of the four Font names as Style names) for this new style. Then you will be asked which font file you wish your new style to be based on. You should respond with any of the four listed above. Next you will be asked to supply a height (in drawing units). If you enter a number then your style will always be that height but if you press "Return" then you will be prompted for a height when you use the style in the DTEXT command.

The width factor specifies whether the letters are to appear "squeezed" (a factor of less than 1.0) or "stretched" (a factor of more than 1.0). The obliquing angle will make the letters lean, a positive angle leans forward and a negative angle backwards. The remaining prompts are self-evident.

An advanced feature of AutoCad allows you to create your own FONT file not just a style but the procedure is not simple.

Exercise

> Devise a text style based on the "complex" font which has an undefined height, a width factor of 0.8 and an obliquing angle of 10 degrees.

Once the STYLE command has been completed, this new style becomes active and all subsequent text uses it. If you wish to revert to a previously defined style, you should select DTEXT and then the "style" option, you can then enter the name of this old style.

Hints & Tips

1) If you only use one or two text heights on a drawing, it can be worth making two styles with your required fixed height (and all other factors the same for consistent appearance). This can avoid having to think about the "height" prompt of the DTEXT command.

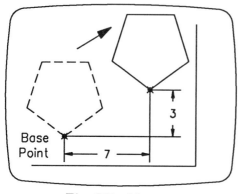

Fig. 5/5 - Move

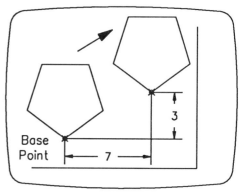

Fig. 5/6 - Copy

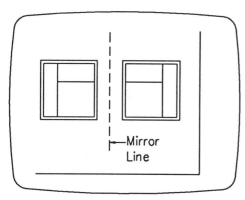

Fig. 5/7 - Mirror

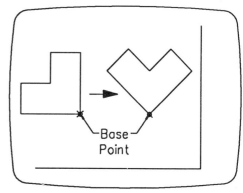

Fig. 5/8 - Rotate

NOTES

MORE EDITING

All the previous editing commands have been concerned with removing or adding details to a drawing. All those discussed below will alter the appearance and/or position of existing objects in the drawing.

MOVE

 As its name suggests, this command will alter the position of objects on the drawing. After you have selected the command and then selected the objects to move by any of the usual methods, you will be asked to select a basepoint which can be regarded as a "handle" with which to pick up the objects. Next you will be asked for the new position of this basepoint or "handle". AutoCad will DRAG the objects with the cursor to their new position.

An alternative method of specifying the displacement is to ignore the prompt for selecting the basepoint and type in the x & y increments by which you want to move the object. For example, entering 7,3 in response to the first prompt and pressing "Return" at the second prompt, will move the object across 7 and up 3. Negative values are quite acceptable.

COPY

 This command is very similar to the MOVE command except that it produces a copy of the original objects in a new position but leaves the original in place.

Exercise

Draw some objects e.g. circles, rectangles, text on the screen then use the MOVE and COPY commands .

MIRROR

This command produces a mirror image of an object or number of objects about a specified mirror line. The mirror line can be at any angle but if you want it to be horizontal or vertical then turn on the ORTHO function.

This facility is particularly useful for changing the "handed-ness" of standard components which have been placed in the drawing using INSERT (see later module).

ROTATE

This is used to rotate an object about a specified base point by a specified angle.

Exercise

Using just a simple asymetric figure e.g. a non-regular polygon, experiment with the MIRROR and ROTATE commands.

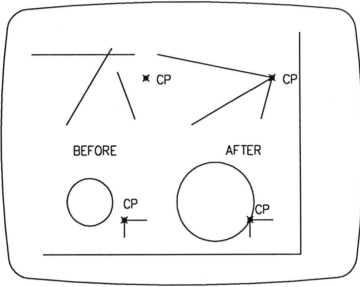

Fig. 5/9 - Changing Objects

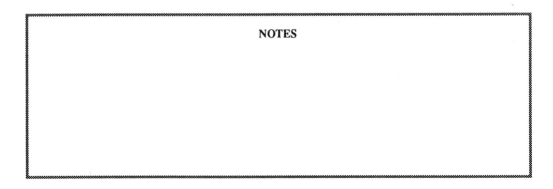

MORE EDITING - CHANGE

The **CHANGE** command is a powerful edit command and because of the large number of options available, it can be tricky to use. Many of the options will not make sense at this stage but some are worthy of investigation.

On selecting the command , you will first be asked to select the objects as usual. Next you will be prompted for the change point or you can overide this by entering "p" for Properties. It is this latter option that you should pass over for the present (it crops up in the module on Layers).

If you fix a point on the screen as the change point then this will have the following effects :-

a) for **LINES** - the nearest endpoint of a line will be moved to the changepoint position.

b) for **CIRCLES** - the circumference is altered to pass through the change point.

c) for **TEXT** - the text will be moved to the new position OR if you press "Return" instead of fixing a change point, then you will be given a repeat of the TEXT command to allow you to change any of the properties of the text.

Exercise

Practice the CHANGE command with some of the three objects listed above.

Hints & Tips

1) If you select a number of lines as objects to CHANGE then the nearest endpoints of each line will be brought to the single new change point.

2) This command can be very useful when editing digitised drawings where, for example, lines that should meet, don't, because of the relative inaccuracy of the digitising process. It can also be used to make true rectangles out of distorted rectangles caused by the same problem.

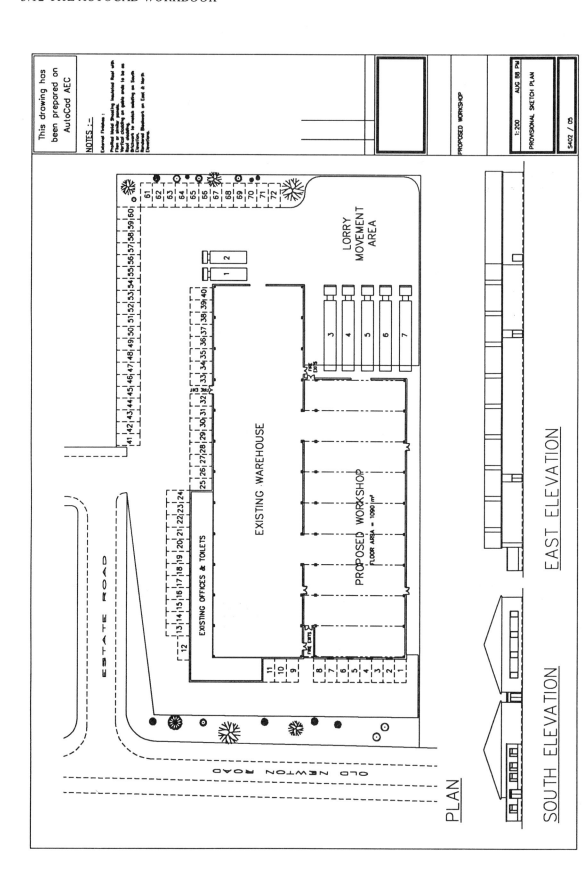

PLAN

SOUTH ELEVATION

EAST ELEVATION

6 : LAYERS, LINETYPES AND COLOURS

PRE-REQUISITE KNOWLEDGE

Before starting this module you should know how to use several of the AutoCad drawing and editing commands and be able to produce labelled drawings using appropriate drawing aids and settings.

OBJECTIVES

After completing this module you should be able to:

1) Use Layers to enhance clarity and promote draughting efficiency.

2) Declare and set relevant layers.

3) Load and scale Linetypes.

4) Assign Colours and Linetypes to layers.

5) Control the visibility of layers.

INTRODUCTION

One extremely useful feature of CAD systems is the use of LAYERS in the production of drawings.

You can visualise each layer as a perfectly transparent sheet of tracing paper . Drawing can take place on any of these sheets. The main difference between CAD layers and real tracing paper is that drawings on layers can be turned "on" and "off" so that the drawing on that layer can be made visible or invisible. Even when it is invisible, the drawing is still there and can be turned "on" at any time.

You would normally only use the layers that were appropriate for the job you were working on at the time because more complex drawings can take a time to regenerate after, say, a ZOOM. By freezing unwanted layers these delays are minimised.

One advantage of preparing drawings on layers, as opposed to showing views side-by-side as in conventional drawings, is that clashes between components becomes obvious. Layers are also of significance at the plotting stage, where unwanted layers can be frozen and will not plot.

It is usual to assign a colour to a layer so that all objects drawn on that layer will be of identical colour. The same is true of different linetypes.

LAYER COMMAND : NEW

AutoCad requires that each layer be given a name or number and this achieved by selecting the "new" option of the LAYER command.

It is good practice to give layers (brief !) meaningful names so that in a drawing with many layers you can remember which layer is which.

Exercise

Select LAYER then "new". Enter a name consisting of letters (and numbers). You will notice that you are still in the LAYER command rather than back at the Command: prompt. This is to allow you to use several options without having to repeatedly select the LAYER command. Get out of the LAYER command by pressing "Return"

You can type in several layer names at one prompt by separating the names with commas.

Exercise

Select LAYER and new again then enter several new layer names in the form PLAN1, PLAN2 etc. Exit the LAYER command.

If you want to check the details of the layers that you have labelled, then select "listing" followed by "all" which will give details of all layers together with their status.In addition to your four layers there should be a LAYER 0. This is the layer that AutoCad automatically uses when you start a new drawing and is always present.

NOTES

LAYER COMMAND : SET

The "set" option of the "LAYER" command specifies the layer on which you are going to draw which is called the "CURRENT" layer and its name is shown on the status line at the top of the screen.

Exercise

Use LAYER then "set" to make one of your layers the current layer. Its name will not appear on the status line until you exit the LAYER command.

LAYER COMMAND : MAKE

The "make" option of the LAYER command combines "new" and "set". If you select this option you can enter the name of a single new layer and when you exit the LAYER command this will automatically become the current layer.

Hints & Tips

1) You will sometimes draw objects on the wrong layer by mistake. This can be easily rectified using the "properties" option of the CHANGE command. When this situation occurs, select CHANGE and then pick the objects that are on the wrong layer. Next choose "properties" then "Layer" and you will be prompted for the name of the new layer.

2) If you realise that there are a couple of lines missing from some part of the drawing and these should be on a different layer to your current layer, then it is quicker to draw them on the current layer then CHANGE them to the correct layer than to "set" the correct layer, draw the lines then re-"set" the current layer.

3) If you are using a monochrome display, it is difficult to see if an object is on the correct layer in which case, use the LIST command. This will ask you to select the object (s) then when you press "Return" the text screen will give information about that object including its Layer.

LAYER COMMAND : COLOR

A different colour can be assigned to each layer of a drawing primarily to improve its clarity. A typical use would be to show ,say, the building services superimposed on a plan of a building with gas in yellow, water in blue and so on.

To implement the colour option offered by the Layer command, the following sequence must be followed :

1) Select LAYER.

2) Select "color".

3) Select the desired colour from the list.

4) Next you will be asked for the layer name to which this colour is to be assigned.

Exercise

Assign different colours to several of your layers.

Use the "listing" then "all" facility to check that all is correct.

It should be mentioned that although AutoCad gives you the choice of colours, your particular set of hardware may not display all of these. For instance the CGA display can only handle four colours so that yellow and white may appear the same on the screen.

The selection of a colour for a layer also has implications for the plotting of a drawing where by using the appropriate pens in the plotter, the final drawing could appear in the same colours as the screen presentation. If you intend to produce the final drawing in different thicknesses of black pen, then at the drafting stage use ,say, red for all thin lines and green for all wide lines. When you come to plot the drawing you will be asked which pen to use for red so make sure your thin pen is used for red and so on.

NOTES

LINETYPES

AutoCad gives you the possibility of using nine different linetypes and you should consult the Help file for a description of these together with its name. It is common practice to use a different layer for each linetype used in a drawing e.g. all centrelines on Layer CL. However, before using any linetype, it must first be loaded. This is accomplished by using the "Load" option of the LINETYPE command which can be found under the SETTINGS heading of the Rootmenu.

Exercise

After consulting the Help file, choose a particular linetype and load it.

Once the linetype has been loaded, then the process of defining which layers are to have which linetype is identical in operation to the "color" option and uses the "ltype" option of the LAYER command.

Exercise

Assign the linetype you have loaded to one of your layers then "set" this layer as the current layer.

If you were to start drawing using this linetype you would not get the anticipated result as the scale of the dots and/or dashes would be unlikely to be correct for your drawing size. The scale of the linetype is adjusted using the LTSCALE command. A certain amount of experimentation is necessary to arrive at a suitable scale factor. If your limits are something like 15000,10000 then a factor of 1000 may be about right but with limits of 12,8 then a factor of 2 might be suitable.

Exercise

Use LTSCALE to enter a scale factor then draw a line on the screen ensuring that you have the correct current layer and examine the effect. If the line appears to be continuous then your factor is too small or too large. Repeat the LTSCALE command until a satisfactory picture is achieved.

LAYER COMMAND : ON/OFF

The visibility of any Layer is controlled by the On/Off option of the LAYER command. Turning it "off" makes it invisible and "on" makes it visible again. This particular option does not alter the regeneration time of the drawing as the computer still does all the calculations required but just does not display the results.

Exercise

Make sure that you have drawn something on each of several layers then experiment with turning some of them "off".

LAYER COMMAND : FREEZE/THAW

The freeze/thaw option is designed to speed up the draughting process when many layers are in use. On a complex drawing, zooming and other commands become slower. In order to minimise this delay, some layers which are not required in the immediate future may be "frozen" which gives the effect that they have ceased to exist thus reducing the computation involved in zooming.

The "frozen" layers have not ceased to exist and can be reinstated by "thaw"'ing them

This command also has effects in the plotting of a drawing when frozen layers will be ignored.

Exercise

You can try freezing some of your layers but unless you have a complex drawing you probably will not notice any difference in the regeneneration time compared to the on/off option.

NOTES

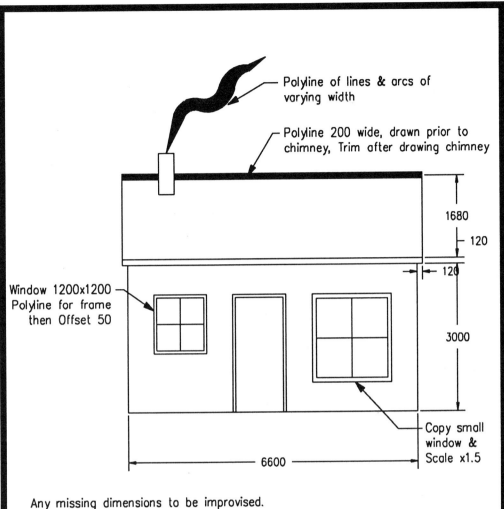

Polyline of lines & arcs of varying width

Polyline 200 wide, drawn prior to chimney, Trim after drawing chimney

1680

120

120

Window 1200x1200 Polyline for frame then Offset 50

3000

Copy small window & Scale x1.5

6600

Any missing dimensions to be improvised.

SETTINGS INFORMATION :

LIMITS – User defined
GRID – 600
SNAP – 300 (When used)
ORTHO – (Mostly) ON
Dimensions are for instruction and need not be appear on final drawing

DRAWING ASSIGNMENT No : 04
DATE COMPLETED : _____
STUDENT INITIALS : _____

THE AUTOCAD WORKBOOK

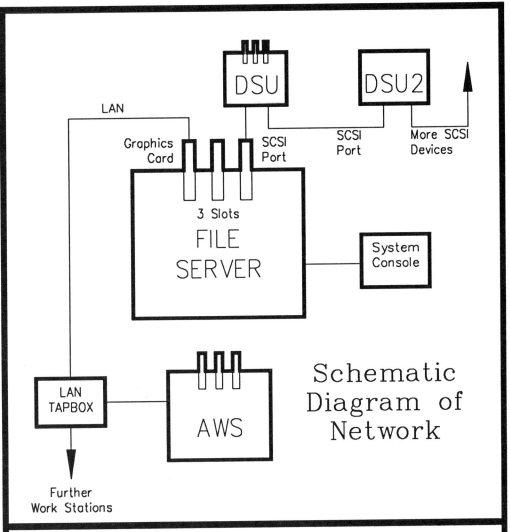

LAN

Graphics
Card

DSU

DSU2

SCSI
Port

SCSI
Port

More SCSI
Devices

3 Slots

FILE
SERVER

System
Console

LAN
TAPBOX

AWS

Schematic
Diagram of
Network

Further
Work Stations

SETTINGS INFORMATION :

You should draw this diagram as if it were to occupy an A4 sheet (210 x 297)
i.e. slightly larger than the drawing above. Outlines of components should be
red polylines, connecting lines are green and text is cyan. You will need to use
most of the ways of positioning text. Arrowheads are polylines with a zero
starting width and finite ending width

DRAWING ASSIGNMENT No : 05
DATE COMPLETED : _____
STUDENT INITIALS : _____

THE AUTOCAD WORKBOOK

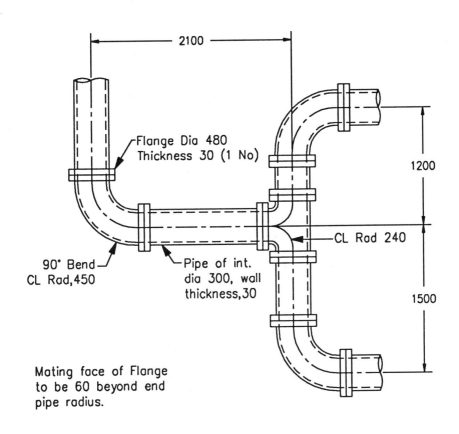

2100

Flange Dia 480
Thickness 30 (1 No)

1200

CL Rad 240

90° Bend
CL Rad, 450

Pipe of int.
dia 300, wall
thickness, 30

1500

Mating face of Flange
to be 60 beyond end
pipe radius.

DRAWING HINTS :

Four Layers (CL, Hidden detail,outline & text) with appropriate linetypes. Draw
Centreline as two Polylines and use offset for pipe walls, Change to correct Layers
Clean up intersections. Draw one pair of flanges and Copy (with Rotate), Trim
outlines that pass through flanges.

DRAWING ASSIGNMENT No : 06
DATE COMPLETED : _____
STUDENT INITIALS : _____

THE AUTOCAD WORKBOOK

7 : CREATING AND USING BLOCKS

PRE-REQUISITE KNOWLEDGE

Before attempting this module , you should be familiar with AutoCad's drawing and editing features.

OBJECTIVES

After completing this module you should be able to:

1) Appreciate the uses of Blocks

2) Create temporary Blocks

3) Create permanent Blocks

4) Insert Blocks into a drawing

5) Use the facility to scale and rotate Blocks

6) Edit existing Blocks

INTRODUCTION

The use of Blocks to define frequently used symbols and components is one of the most important and time-saving features of CAD systems.

There is no limit on what can be made into a Block and common examples might include title-blocks, mechanical & electronic components, architectural features etc.

Users can build up libraries of drawings of frequently used components and other features from which they can retrieve these details to use in new drawings. In order to streamline the process further, manufacturers are beginning to issue disks containing drawings of their products for use by draftspersons.

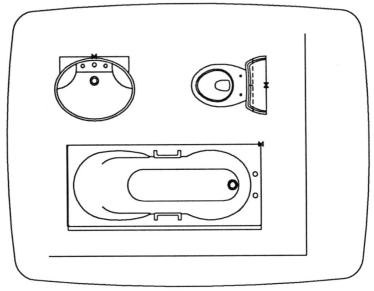

Fig. 7/1 - Blocks issued by Ideal Standard

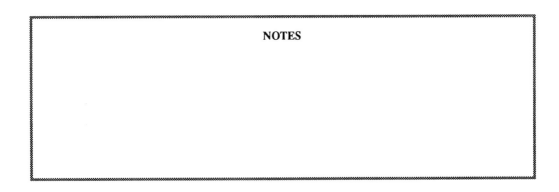

NOTES

BLOCKS

Just a brief explanation of some of the terminology involved before you start the exercise :

    1) A **"BLOCK"** is any detail, part of a drawing or complete drawing that can be saved for later re-use.

    2) The process of recalling and using a detail is known as "**INSERT**ing" a block.

    3) Any block may contain graphical information, text (including dimensions) and non-graphical details of the block e.g. price, manufacturer's product code. These non-graphical details are called **"ATTRIBUTES"** and their use is outside the scope of this book.

BLOCK COMMAND : INSERTION POINT

In order to position a block on a new drawing, it is necessary to define a point on the block when it is created called the **"INSERTION POINT".** When inserted on a new drawing the block will be placed with its insertion point at the location that the user specifies.

BLOCKS COMMAND : CREATING A BLOCK

You will notice that there are two similar commands on the menu under the heading of BLOCKS, namely **"BLOCK"** and "**WBLOCK".**

"BLOCK" creates a block which is held in the computer's memory for the duration of this drawing session. When the computer is switched off this will be lost i.e. it is a temporary block. This can be useful for moving parts of drawings around or where a component will appear several times on that particular drawing but will not be required at a later date. If the drawing is "SAVEed", the definition of the Block is saved with it and will be re-loaded when you re-load the drawing.

"WBLOCK" creates a block which is saved to a floppy or hard disk and will always be available from that source i.e. a permanent block.

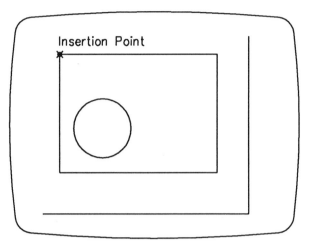

Fig. 7/2 - Insertion Point of a Block

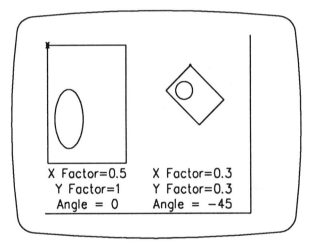

Fig. 7/3 - Scaled & Rotated Blocks

NOTES

BLOCK

We will first examine the "BLOCK" variation.

Exercise

First you must draw something to be used as a block. It is suggested that a simple figure consisting of a circle inside a rectangle would be suitable.

Then the procedure is as follows :-

1) Select "BLOCK" and you will be asked for a name for the block.

2) Enter a name you will remember e.g. SQUIRCLE.

3) You will now be asked for an insertion point, so position the cursor over a point on the drawing e.g. the bottom left corner, and press the left mouse button (or use OSNAP).

4) Next you will be asked for details about what you want to include in your block. You should select the objects by any of the usual methods.

5) On completion of the selection, the drawing will disappear as it becomes a block. AutoCad removes the block from the screen and in order to retrieve it, select (or type in) OOPS and it will re-appear.

BLOCKS COMMAND : INSERT

Now that you have created a block, we will INSERT it into your drawing.

Exercise

1) Select"INSERT".

2) The prompt will ask you for a block name, to which you can respond with the block you have just created.

3) Next you will be asked for the insertion point, so you can either :- a) fix a point on the drawing screen OR b) select "drag" which will allow you to move the block around the screen before finally fixing its position.

4) The next two prompts allow you to alter the size of the block to suit the drawing. For instance you may have created a block using metres as your drawing unit, if you were to insert this into a drawing which used millimetres then the block would be 1000 times too small. Declaring an X scale factor of less than 1 reduces the block size and vica versa. For this exercise, try a factor of 0.5 for both X and Y.

5) The final prompt allows you to rotate the block about its insertion point to achieve the correct orientation. Angles are in degrees measured anticlockwise. Try 45.

6) INSERT the same block with different scale factors and rotations.

NOTES

BLOCKS COMMAND : WBLOCK

Next we will save a permanent block using the "WBLOCK" command. (WBLOCK stands for Write BLOCK to a file). This procedure is almost the same as that for a "BLOCK" except for the following :-

1) The first prompt after selecting the "WBLOCK" option asks for a file name which is the name under which it will be held on disc. This name may have to include the drive letter where the block is to be saved e.g. A:SQUIRCLE. If no drive is specified it will be saved to the directory and drive that is currently in use.

2) The second prompt is "Block Name" which allows you to make a permanent WBLOCK from a previously declared temporary BLOCK.

3) The remaining prompts are identical to those for a temporary block.

NB If you are using a training version of AutoCad you may not be able to save a WBLOCK to disc: in which case you will not be able to carry out the exercise below.

Exercise

Create a drawing possibly with some text then save it as a WBLOCK.

INSERTing a WBLOCK is identical to that for inserting a BLOCK.

Exercise

Insert the WBLOCK you have just created.

BLOCKS COMMAND : Hints & Tips

1) AutoCad treats blocks as a single object which cannot be edited and can only be erased in its entirety.

Exercise

Try erasing one of the blocks you have inserted. When prompted to select objects, just pick one line of the block and it will all be shown ghosted.

2) This could be very inconvenient if you wanted to edit just a small detail. There are two possible solutions to this :-

a) Type in a " * " immediately before the block name in the insertion process e.g. *SQUIRCLE or * A:SQUIRCLE. This will insert the block in the pieces with which it was originally created and it can then be edited in the usual way.

b) Use the EXPLODE command on a block that has been inserted in the normal way i.e. without a " * ". Blocks which have differing scale factors in the x & y directions cannot be exploded.

Exercise

Try both of the above methods to erase just one line of a block.

3) If your blocks have been created on Layer 0, they can be inserted on to any other layer. However if a block is created on a layer other than 0 then it will automatically bring this (or these) layer(s) with it when it is inserted. This can lead to a rapid and unwanted proliferation of layers or can be convenient if you use a "standard" layering system.

4) If you were to list the drawing files on a disk, you would find that both complete drawings and wblocks had file names which included the extension .DWG which AutoCad has specified e.g. SQUIRCLE.DWG. This is one indication that whole drawings can be inserted as blocks even though this might not have been the original intention. This can be useful if, for example, a set of drawings included a large scale location plan which also appears at a smaller scale on other drawings. In this case the large scale plan would be prepared as normal then it could be inserted with reducing scale factors, as a block in other drawings.

8 : HATCHING, EXTRACTING INFORMATION AND
MORE EDITING

PRE-REQUISITE KNOWLEDGE

Before attempting this module , you should be familiar with a number of AutoCad's drawing and editing features specifically Layers and Polylines.

OBJECTIVES

After completing this module you should be able to:

1) Create and use simple hatching.

2) Scale and use more complex hatch patterns.

3) Display information about the system.

4) List, Copy and Rename files.

5) Measure features on a drawing.

6) Use the editing commands ARRAY, DIVIDE, MEASURE, SCALE, STRETCH and EXTEND.

INTRODUCTION

One of the most time consuming and tedious activities in conventional drafting is hatching areas. Only simple patterns are attempted by hand and (expensive) Letraset is necessary for complicated patterns. Autocad has a large number of standard hatch patterns as well as simple lined hatching.

It can be very useful to remind yourself of the settings and state of its various parameters in your present drawing and AutoCad provides a means of doing this.

The drawings for any project form the basis for further documentation in the form of lists of components or bills of quantities. You can measure lengths and areas directly from the drawing screen with a high degree of accuracy to obtain quantities for bills.

As with previous modules, you will also be introduced to some more of AutoCad's editing features.

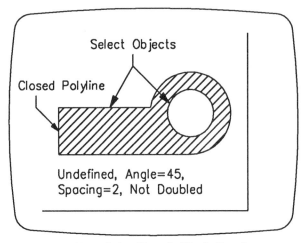

Fig. 8/1 - Hatch-Undefined

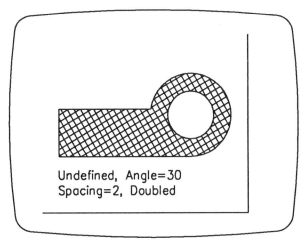

Fig. 8/2 - Hatch-Undefined-Double

NOTES

HATCHING

Many drawings require different surfaces or areas to be drawn with a pattern on them which might indicate the type of material or machining. In practice the AutoCad HATCH command can be a bit unreliable as, for example hatching can "bleed" out of an area with unpredictable results. Sometimes the hatching may run over an internal feature of the hatched area. The process given below may not be the fastest but it is the most reliable. You can always try the "straight" method and if it doesn't work then use this method below.

The only object whose boundary is totally unambiguous is a closed Polyline (which includes Circles, Ellipses & Polygons) and this fact is utilised as follows:-

1) Make a layer on which to place the hatching (called HATCHED or something similar). This will also allow you to plot the hatching with a different colour or pen size.

2) Make another layer called HATCHOUT where you will place the outlines to be hatched. This layer can be frozen prior to plotting.

3) Make the HATCHOUT the current layer.

4) Decide which area you want to hatch and "trace" the outline on to your HATCHOUT layer as a closed POLYLINE. Setting OSNAP to "INTersec" can speed this up.

5) Set the HATCHED layer and freeze all layers except HATCHOUT and HATCHED.

6) Use the HATCH command :-

i) to load and then use a standard AutoCad hatch pattern (see later)

OR

ii) to define and use a simple parallel line type of hatch pattern. This option is selected by entering "u" (for "undefined") at the prompt. You will then be asked for the angle for the lines, the spacing between lines and whether you want the pattern to be repeated in mirror image i.e. Double hatch area.

Exercise

> Create suitable layers then draw (or "trace") a closed PLINE. Select HATCH and using the "u" option, hatch in your figure. When complete use ERASE, "last" to remove it and try a different angle/spacing/Double combination.

Hints & Tips

1) The spacing is defined in drawing units and using too small a spacing may result in a very long wait for the hatching to be completed. Always err on the side of "too big" to start with and reduce the spacing if necessary.

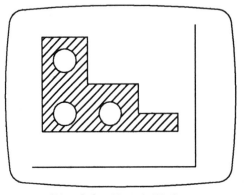

Fig. 8/3 - Hatch-U,O

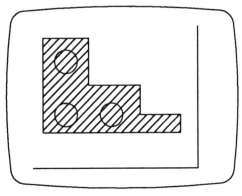

Fig. 8/4 - Hatch-U, I

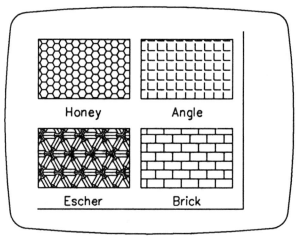

Fig. 8/5 - Hatch Patterns

NOTES

MORE HATCHING

Often hatched areas will contain holes or other features that are not required to be hatched. AutoCad often avoids holes automatically but you can insist on this by entering ",O" after "U" (or any other hatch pattern). "O" stands for "Outermost area only".

Using "I" in place of the "O" means "Ignore inner structure" and will hatch over any holes or features.

Exercise

On your HATCHED layer, create a figure consisting of a closed PLINE e.g. a rectangle with a CIRCLE inside it. Then use the "u,o" option to hatch around the hole. When you are prompted to "Select Objects", pick the outline and the hole. ERASE this and select "u,i" to hatch over the hole.

AutoCad is supplied with a number of standard hatch patterns (in a file called ACAD.PAT). You can obtain a list of these pattern names from the HATCH command by entering "?" in response to the "Pattern" prompt. The AutoCad manual gives drawings of these patterns along with their names. A few are shown on the facing page.

You can use any of these by entering the relevant pattern name at the "Pattern" prompt (with ",O" or ",I" if required). Next you will be asked for a scale for the hatch pattern and a certain amount of experimentation is necessary to arrive at a suitable figure. As previously, start with a large factor and decrease it if necessary. You are then asked for an angle through which the pattern can be rotated.

Exercise

Draw a number of CIRCLEs and hatch in each with a different pattern. Create a figure with a hole as in the previous exercise and try hatching with standard patterns and the "O" and "I" options.

```
              LINE      Layer:  0
           from point,  X=        70   Y=         41
             to point,  X=       100   Y=         70
               Length  =         42,  Angle  =       44
               Delta X =         30,  Delta Y =          29

   11 entities in aw0802
Limits are          X:          0        210  (Off)
                    Y:          0        297
Drawing uses        X:         20        185
                    Y:         10        285
Display shows       X:          0        425
                    Y:          0        297
Insertion base is   X:     0    Y:        0    Z:         0
Snap resolution is  X:     5    Y:        5
Grid spacing is     X:    10    Y:       10

Current layer:      OUTLINE
Current color:      BYLAYER -- 7 (white)
Current linetype: BYLAYER -- CONTINUOUS
Current elevation:        0   thickness:          0
Axis off  Fill on  Grid on  Ortho off  Qtext off  Snap off  Tablet off
Object snap modes: None
Free RAM: 10124 bytes        Free disk: 3653632 bytes
I/O page space:   92K bytes
```

Fig. 8/6 - List (top) & Status (bottom)

NOTES

INQUIRY - STATUS, TIME, LIST & DBLIST

The STATUS command can be used at any time and will report the settings of a whole series of commands such as LIMITS, GRID, LAYER, COLOUR etc. It will also state how many objects are present in a drawing and how much disk space there is left.

Exercise

Select INQUIRY then STATUS to view the settings for your present drawing.

TIME displays information on the period that the drawing has been worked on. This can be useful for filling in timesheets and allocating operators time to various projects.

Exercise

Select TIME and view the information.

LIST will display the information that defines a particular object on a drawing. For Polylines it will give all the information about each segment of a Polyline.

Exercise

Draw a LINE, a CIRCLE and a PLINE then use LIST and examine the output.

DBLIST is similar to LIST except that it displays a list of all the objects in a drawing i.e. all the objects in the AutoCad DataBase. This can be a lengthy process unless the drawing is simple.

Exercise

Assuming your drawing only contains only a few objects, select DBLIST.

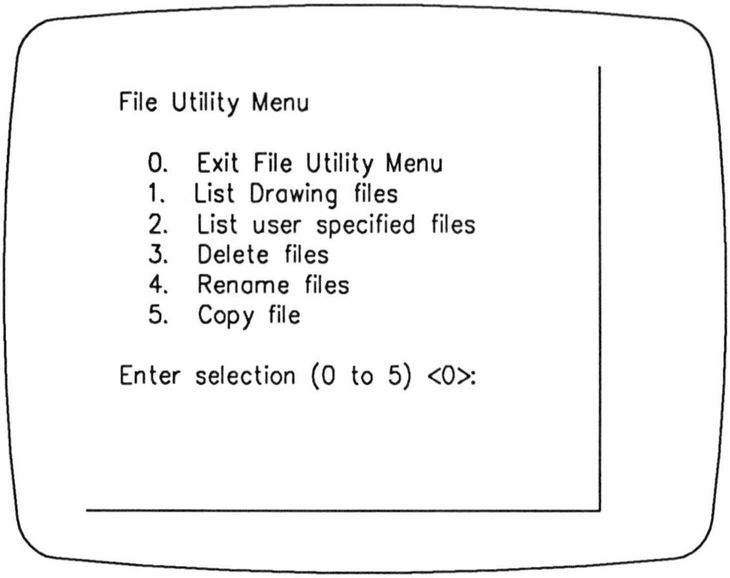

```
File Utility Menu

     0.   Exit File Utility Menu
     1.   List Drawing files
     2.   List user specified files
     3.   Delete files
     4.   Rename files
     5.   Copy file

Enter selection (0 to 5) <0>:
```

Fig. 8/7 - Files Menu

NOTES

FILES MENU

AutoCad provides a facility to list files and to carry out some operations on them. All these options can be performed at the DOS level i.e. before loading AutoCad or after exiting AutoCad and details of this are given in Appendix A. However you may wish to remain in AutoCad, in which case the Files menu is available as Option 6 on the Main Menu or can be accessed at any time by entering the command "FILES".

Exercise

> Assuming you are working on a drawing, then enter FILES. The section below explains the options which you are offered.

1) List Drawing files - Will display a list of all AutoCad drawing files in the drive\directory you specify. If you press "Return" in response to the prompt asking for the directory, the files in the current directory will be provided.

2) List user specified files - Allows you to specify a range of files (not necessarily Drawing files) to be listed e.g. to list all AutoLisp files in the current directory, you would specify

*.LSP

or to list Drawing files for a certain project whose filenames all begin with LLEA on drive A: , you would use

A:\LLEA*.DWG

3) Delete files - Asks for the filenames to be deleted and if you use the wildcard symbol *, each file that complies with your definition will be listed for you to confirm that you do indeed wish to delete it.

4) Rename files - Permits you to alter the filename of any file.

5) Copy file - Allows you to copy any one file from a specified drive\directory to another drive\directory (and to change the name in the process).

Exercise

> Try out some of these options but be careful which files you delete or rename. A previous drawing exercise file would be suitable; do not delete or rename any AutoCad program file.

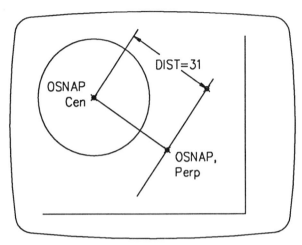

Fig. 8/8 - Measuring Distance (using Osnap)

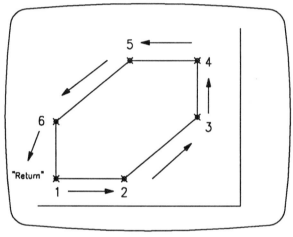

Fig. 8/9 - Measuring Area

NOTES

MEASURING OBJECTS - DIST & AREA

The commands DIST, for measuring distances between two points, and AREA, for measuring the areas of shapes are extremely useful and relatively straightforward to use.

The DIST command requires either :-

i) Two points to be fixed on the drawing area (possibly used in conjunction with OSNAP).

OR

ii) Selection of an object which has an unambiguous length e.g. a LINE, a CIRCLE etc.

The AREA command requires either :-

i) The fixing of a number of points on the drawing area (using OSNAP if necessary) and pressing "Return" terminates the selection.

OR

ii) The selection of a closed figure such as a CIRCLE, ELLIPSE or closed PLINE. N.B: A number of LINES forming a closed figure is not acceptable.

Exercise

Using a number of LINES, CIRCLES and closed PLINES, select INQUIRY then DIST or AREA, examine the displayed information. Note the accuracy.

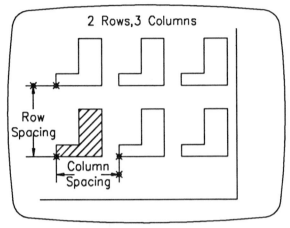

Fig. 8/12 - Array-Rectangular

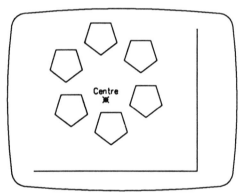

Fig. 8/10 - Array-Polar, not rotated

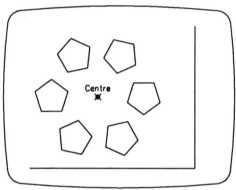

Fig. 8/11 - Array-Polar, rotated

NOTES

MORE EDITING : ARRAY

The ARRAY command allows you to make multiple copies of an object in the drawing. These copies can be arranged in a rows/columns configuration or alternatively in a circular arrangement.

On selecting the command, you will be asked for the object(s) to copy and you should select them in the usual manner. Next you will be asked to choose between Rectangular and Polar i.e. circular Arrays.

ARRAY - Rectangular

You will be asked how many rows and columns of the original object you require. This number should include the original object. Next you will be asked for a spacing between rows/columns. This dimension is the distance from a point on the original object to the corresponding point on a copy. It is not the clear space between objects. Positive distances will be UP or to the RIGHT of the original and negative distances will be below or to the left of the original.

Exercise

> Near the bottom left corner of the drawing area, create a simple shape e.g. a polygon. Select EDIT then ARRAY and produce an array with three rows and four columns. Choose a suitable spacing to keep the array within the drawing limits.

ARRAY - Polar

Polar Arrays :- In this option, you will be asked for the centre point of the array then you will answer any two of the next three prompts which decide on the number of copies to be made and their spacing. Any two replies specifies a unique pattern.

> Prompt 1 : Number of copies in the array
>
> Prompt 2 : The angle occupied by the whole array
>
> Prompt 3 : The angle between successive copies

The sign convention is +ve angles are Counter ClockWise (CCW) and -ve angles are ClockWise (CW).

The final prompt asks you whether you wish the object to be rotated as AutoCad makes the copies. See facing page.

Exercise

> Create a simple object away from the edges of the drawing area and then produce a polar array. Repeat the process using different methods of specifying the extent of the array.

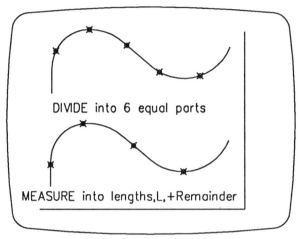

Fig. 8/13 - Divide & Measure

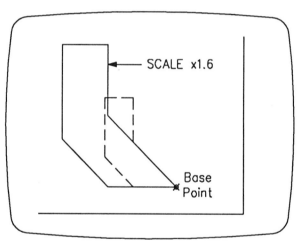

Fig. 8/14 - Scaling an object

NOTES

MORE EDITING : DIVIDE, MEASURE & SCALE

DIVIDE & MEASURE

Both of these commands mark an existing LINE, ARC, CIRCLE or PLINE into equal length sections. This can be useful to join on other objects using the points given by these commands as "nodes" in OSNAP.

DIVIDE marks the object into a specified number of sections of equal length.

MEASURE marks the object into specified equal lengths.

Both of these commands can be used to insert a Block at the points located by the commands. Full details of this can be found in the AutoCad manual.

Exercise

Draw a LINE, an ARC, a CIRCLE and a PLINE across the top half of the drawing area. Then COPY these to the lower half of the screen. Use DIVIDE on the upper collection and MEASURE on the lower group.

SCALE

This command is nothing to do with the scale of the drawing for plotting purposes but allows you to re-size an existing object. The scale factor is applied equally to the x and y dimensions.

It is necessary to define a point on the drawing (not necessarily on the object) which will remain in the same place after re- sizing. This is the BasePoint.

You can enter a scale factor when prompted but as this might require some calculation, if you enter "R" at this prompt you can specify an original i.e. Reference length and a new length, then AutoCad will compute the scale factor for you and execute the re- sizing.

Exercise

Draw a POLYGON and then re-size it using the SCALE command.

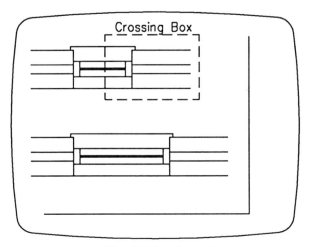

Fig. 8/15 - Stretch

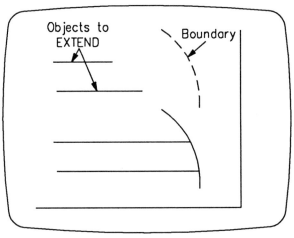

Fig. 8/16 - Extend

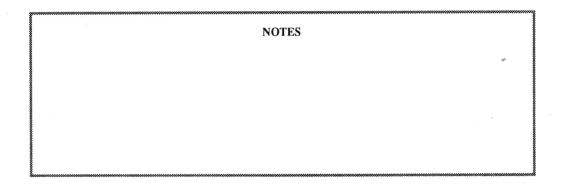

NOTES

MORE EDITING : STRETCH and EXTEND

The STRETCH command allows you to move an object(s) and all other lines joined to it will be adjusted to maintain their connection with the object(s).

You always use a "window" or "crossing" mode to select the object to be moved. Any object that is entirely within the window will be moved and any object which has an endpoint outside the window will be stretched. Its endpoint outside the window will remain in the same position. Blocks cannot be STRETCHed unless they have been EXPLODEd.

Exercise

Draw a rectangle with a LINE extending outwards from two corners, an ARC from one corner and a PLINE from the last corner. Select EDIT then STRETCH and ensure your rectangle is entirely within the window but the endpoints of the other lines are outside. Choose a Basepoint on the rectangle and then a New Point at a different location and observe the result.

EXTEND is used to increase the length of an object up to a boundary. This is quicker than adding, say, another Line to make up the gap. This latter approach also increases the number of objects in the drawing which is generally not a desirable effect.

Exercise

Draw a number of unconnected LINES and PLINES and use EXTEND. Try this with an ARC and note the result.

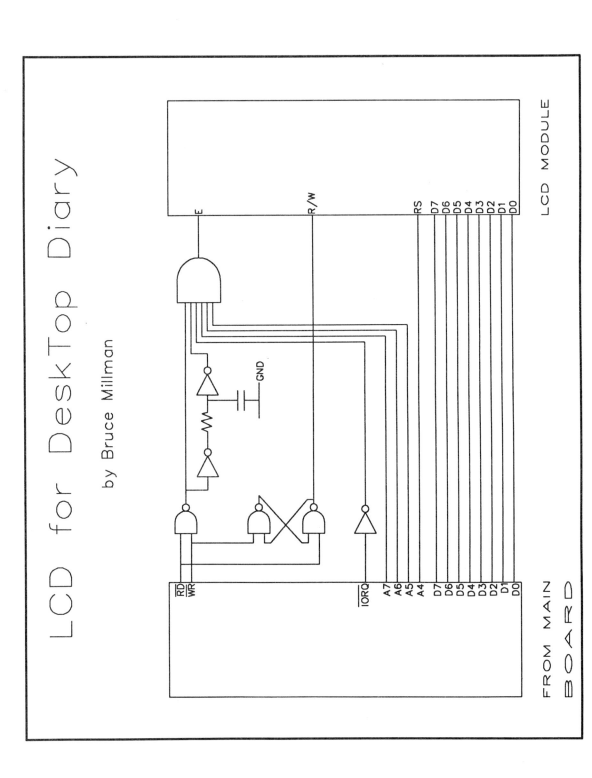

LCD for DeskTop Diary

by Bruce Millman

9 : DIMENSIONING DRAWINGS

PRE-REQUISITE KNOWLEDGE

Before starting this module you should be able to prepare an AutoCad drawing using a variety of drawing and editing commands.

OBJECTIVES

After completing this module you should be able to:

1) Set an appropriate scale for dimensioning.

2) Employ linear dimensioning techniques.

3) Employ circular dimensioning techniques.

4) Appreciate the concept of dimension variables.

5) Set some dimension variables to relevant values.

INTRODUCTION

The dimensioning of an AutoCad drawing can be extremely quick and accurate once the desired style of dimensioning has been set up. This style will probably be a "house" style and will be used on all drawings from the same office or on a single project. The specification of a style is a bit complicated but should only need to be done at infrequent intervals.

Adding dimensions to a drawing is made as convenient as possible because AutoCad knows the value of the dimension and will provide it for you. You only have to specify what to dimension and where it is to appear.

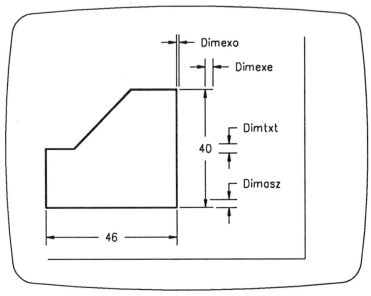

Fig. 9/1 - Examples of Dimvars

NOTES

DIMENSIONING : DIM & DIM1

The AutoCad dimensioning command DIM is like the LAYER command in the respect that once it has been selected, you will remain in it until, in this case, you enter "EXIT". The assumption is that you will wish to dimension several items but if you only wish to add one dimension then you should use the DIM1 command.

The dimension variables, which can be examined or changed with the DIMVARS command, control the appearance of the dimension lines and the format of the dimension values. The diagram on the facing page indicates a few of the variables that you might want to change.

AutoCad is supplied with the dimension variables set at certain values, which being an American product, are most suitable for drawings in feet and inches. However the quickest way to start using the DIM command is to avoid individual variables at the moment and to use the DIMSCALE option to supply an overall scale factor for all relevant variables.

The table below gives a guide to the suitable value of "dimscale".

LIMITS	dimscale
15 x 10	0.1
150 x 100	1.0
1500 x 1000	10.0
15000 x 10000	100.0

Exercise

Select DIM then "dimvars" then "dimscale". Enter a suitable value for your particular LIMITS.

In order to dimension an object, AutoCad has to be told what sort of dimension i.e. Linear, Angular, Diameter or Radius . Then there are several more prompts that require your response.

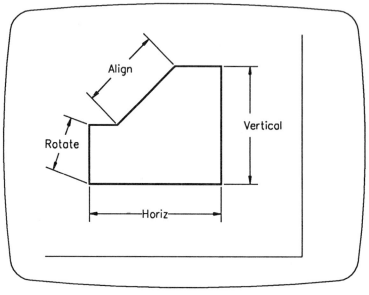

Fig. 9/2 - Linear Dimensioning

NOTES

DIMENSIONING : LINEAR

We will start the use of dimensions by considering a few of the options for Linear dimensions.

After setting the dimscale, if you select "LINEAR" you will then be asked for the orientation of the dimension, and at this stage we will restrict the choice to "horizontal" and "vertical". Once this has been defined, you will be asked for the start point of the first extension line which you should indicate with the mouse, then repeat this for the start of the second extension line. Next you will be asked for the position of the dimension line itself. AutoCad then asks for the value of the dimension and prompts you with the value it expects. Press "Return" to confirm (or type in an alternative value).

Exercise

Draw a rectangle and dimension each of its sides.

The "aligned" and "rotated" options allow you to dimension lines that are not horizontal or vertical. "Aligned" draws the dimension parallel to the start points of the extension lines and "rotated" draws the dimension line at a specified angle.

Exercise

Draw a triangle with a horizontal base and one sloping side at 45 degrees. Dimension the 45 degree side using the "rotated" option, the other sloping side using the "aligned" option and the base using the "horizontal" option.

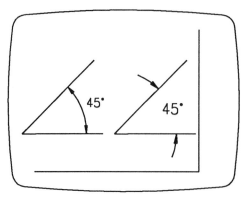

Fig. 9/3 - Angular Dimensions

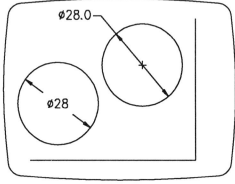

Fig. 9/4 - Diameter Dimensions

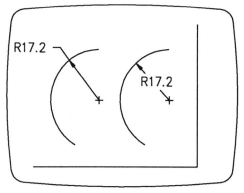

Fig. 9/5 - Radius Dimensions

NOTES

DIMENSIONING : ANGULAR, DIAMETER & RADIUS

If you have grasped the manner in which the "LINEAR" dimensions are declared then you should be able to use the other options Angular, Diameter and Radius without too much guidance.

Exercise

Use the "Angular" option to dimension the angles of the triangle you drew for the previous exercise.

Exercise

Draw a number of circles of varying size and use the "Diameter" and "Radius" options to dimension them.

You may have noticed in the last exercise that for smaller circles the dimension was shown outside the circle. AutoCad decides on where to write the dimension, either inside or outside, on the basis of whether it can fit the dimension line, the arrows and the text within the circle or not. If you wish to force a particular style then suitable adjustment of the "dimscale" can accomplish this but you must bear in mind the appearance of the final plotted drawing and its legibility. Using a small "dimscale" might put all the dimension within a circle but it might also be too small to read on the plot.

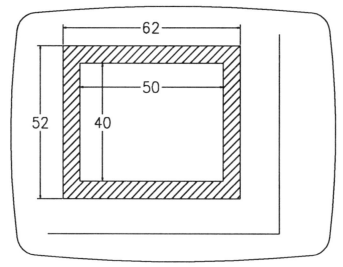

Fig. 9/6 - External and Internal Dimensions

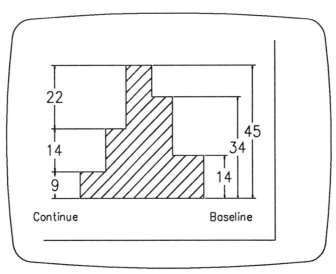

Fig. 9/7 - Continue & Baseline Options

NOTES

DIMENSIONING : DIMVARS

Exercise

> Select DIM then STATUS.

You have just listed the settings of all the dimensioning variables and you can see that there are a considerable number. For a complete explanation you should consult the AutoCad manual however we will initially examine two of the most commonly adjusted variables, namely, "dimtxt" and "dimasz".

The size of the dimension text is controlled by the "dimtxt" variable and the size of the arrowheads by "dimasz".

Exercise

> Draw a number of identical horizontal lines spaced at intervals down the screen (using ARRAY). Dimension each line with a different "dimtxt" and/or "dimasz" using the values given by the previous exercise as a guide. Examine the results.

Two other "dimvars" that are worth examining are Dimse1 and Dimse2. These control whether extension lines are displayed. For internal dimensions of an object, the dimension line touches the object so rendering extension lines unnecessary. Dimse1 and Dimse2 suppress the first and second extension lines when they are set to "ON".

Exercise

> Draw a rectangle and dimension it externally then alter Dimse1 and Dimse2 and dimension it internally.

Using suitable "dimvars" settings virtually any dimensioning style can be achieved including displaying tolerances, dimensions in two units e.g. mm and inches and different text styles.

AutoCad also provides several options for speeding up the dimensioning and these include :-

i) Continue : This facilitates the insertion of a string of dimensions along a line.

ii) Baseline : This allows several dimensions to be related to a single extension line.

iii) Associative dimensioning : With this option active then dimensions will be automatically updated if subsequent stretching, rotating or scaling of the object occurs.

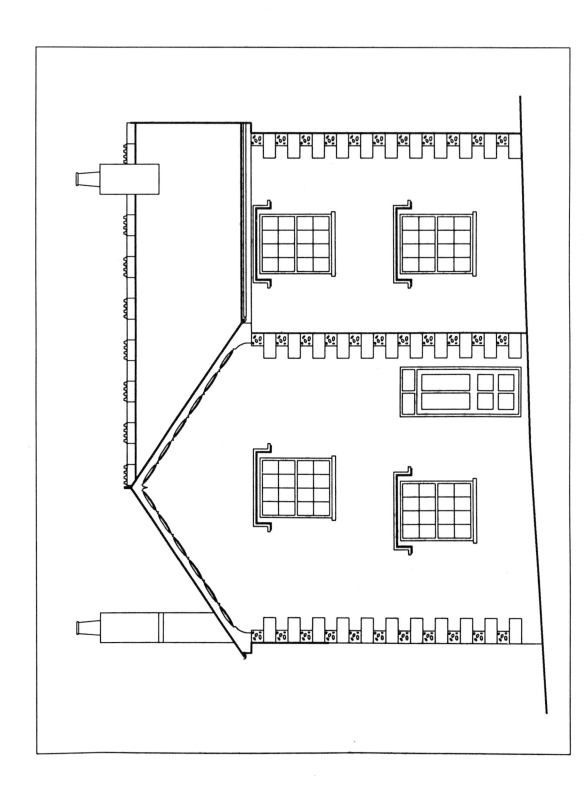

10 : 3-D VISUALISATION

PRE-REQUISITE KNOWLEDGE

Before starting this module you should be familiar with the usual AutoCad 2-D drafting process.

OBJECTIVES

After completing this module you should be able to:

1) Set the relevant AutoCad parameters for 3-D drawing.

2) Produce simple extruded shapes.

3) Draw 3-D lines and faces.

4) View the drawing from any position.

5) Remove hidden lines.

INTRODUCTION

AutoCad's 3-D facility is better described as a visualisation rather than a true model as discussed in the Introduction.

Having said that, some interesting and impressive 3-D drawings can be created. These will be of the wire-frame appearance with distant parts visible through nearer parts but hidden lines can be removed by AutoCad once a particular view is chosen. These 3-D drawings can be exported to other software (Auto-Shade) where colouring and shading of faces can be done.

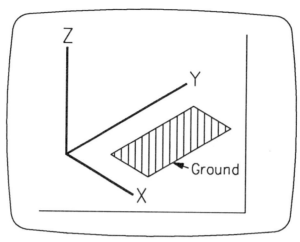

Fig. 10/1 - 3D Coordinates

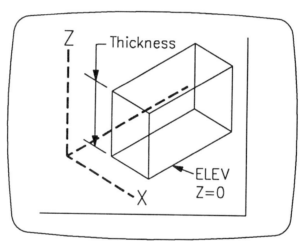

Fig. 10/2 - Elev & Thickness

NOTES

3-D DRAUGHTING : ELEV & THICKNESS

The process of drawing a 3-D object in AutoCad consists of drawing a 2-D shape on the "ground" and telling AutoCad how high to make the object. The plan view is then "extruded" to this height. This approach restricts you to having flat tops on any object however this version of AutoCad also permits you to draw sloping faces and lines and this facility can be used to alter the top of any object.

Thus any shape can be drawn in the x,y plane as in normal 2-D draughting having first specified the z dimension. You can also adjust the height of the "ground" plane to be above the true x,y plane (for which z=0).

This height of the "ground" plane is specified by the ELEV command and the extrusion thickness is set by the THICKNESS option offered with Elev. Initially the elevation and thickness are set at zero and before starting drawing these should be set at the desired value.

Exercise

For this module you need LIMITS of about 8000,6000. Select 3D, then ELEV and the height of extrusion . Press "Return" at the first prompt (leaving the "ground" at z=0) then enter 3000 for the thickness. Select DRAW then LINE and construct a rectangle.

As you are drawing in plan view you will not be able to see if this has created a box 3000 high as anticipated. The next section will discuss changing your viewpoint.

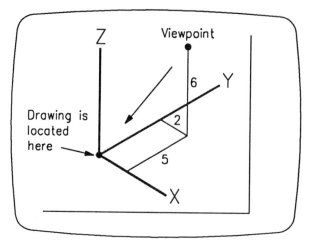

Fig. 10/3 - Viewpoint

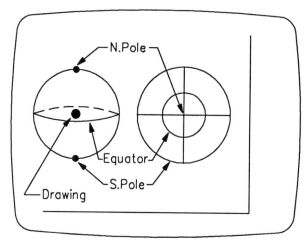

Fig. 10/4 - "Real" Globe & Bullseye

NOTES

3-D DRAUGHTING - VIEWPOINT

In order to understand the viewpoint concept it is necessary to imagine another set of x,y & z axes (not the axes used for preparing the drawing) with your drawing located at the origin. When you are drawing in plan your viewpoint is directly above the origin i.e. x=0 and y=0 but z will have a value. The diagram facing shows the viewpoint defined by 2,5,6. Negative values are quite acceptable.

It should be noted that it is only the relative values of x,y & z that is significant. The view given by 0,0,1 is identical to 0,0,3 or 1,2,1 is the same as 3,6,3. Your distance from the object is controlled by the ZOOM command in the conventional way.

Exercise

Select 3D then VPOINT then enter 1,1,1 and you will see your box in 3-D. Try some other combinations of numbers and examine the result.

The entering of a new Viewpoint by the above method is not very convenient so AutoCad provides two alternative ways of doing this. These are found by selecting the "axes" option of the VPOINT command. When this is chosen, the screen will change to display a set of x,y & z axes and a "bullseye" type of target. It is this latter "bullseye" which is most useful.

The "bullseye" represents a globe which has your drawing at its centre. The North Pole is at the centre of the diagram. The next ring out represents the Equator and the outer ring is the South Pole. You will have to imagine the Southern hemisphere, which would normally be invisible, having been "opened out". By fixing a position on this globe with the mouse, you will define a new viewpoint. This concept seems difficult at first but becomes much easier with use.

Exercise

View your box from a number of different viewpoints using the globe to select them.

Selecting VPOINT then "plan" gives you the normal drawing view i.e. from the North Pole.

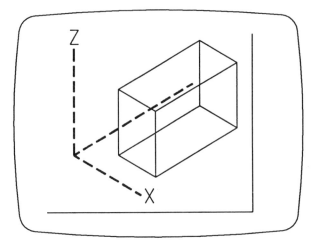

Fig. 10/5 - Wire-Frame View

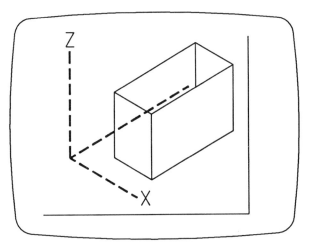

Fig. 10/6 - Same View after Hide

NOTES

3-D DRAUGHTING : HIDE & MORE DRAWING

The picture of your box that you have been getting has been a wire-frame with all lines visible. AutoCad also allows you to remove hidden lines once you have selected a viewpoint. This hidden line removal can be lengthy process with a complex drawing (taking possibly 15 minutes or longer) so when you select the command HIDE you will be asked for confirmation.

Exercise

> Choose a viewpoint other than plan for your box and then select HIDE.

It might appear that AutoCad's 3-D facility is fairly restrictive in its ability to display complex objects but by combining simple 3-D objects such as boxes, cylinders and extruded polygons, it is possible to build up quite realistic models. (Release 9 has more complex "building blocks" like spheres, cones etc)

Exercise

> You are now going to add a cylinder on top of your box. First use VPOINT then "plan" to obtain the plan view. Now set ELEV to 3000 (i.e. the top of the box) and thickness to 2000. Draw a circle inside the rectangle. Change viewpoint to see the result. Then try HIDE.

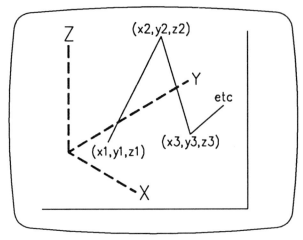

Fig. 10/7 - 3D Lines

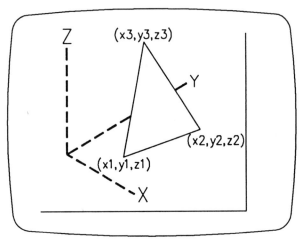

Fig. 10/8 - 3D Face

NOTES

3-D DRAUGHTING : 3-D LINES AND 3-D FACES

In the system outlined so far, drawing is carried out in the x,y plane having pre-set the z coordinate. This version of AutoCad includes the ability to specify lines and faces by entering x,y & z coordinates.

A 3-D LINE is drawn by entering all three coordinates of the endpoints of the line.

Exercise

To draw a line from one of the top corners of your box, determine the x & y coordinates of a corner (using ID). The z coordinate will be 3000. Select 3D LINE and enter the first point as x,y,3000. Enter suitable coordinates for the other endpoint of the line. Change viewpoint to see the result.

3-D FACES are defined by the x,y & z coordinates of their corners. This command builds up a 3-D face from triangular units so it is important to enter the corners in the correct order.

Exercise

Erase all objects from your original drawing then select 3D FACE. If you enter the four points given below in list order you will end up with a rectangular face :-

a) 0,0,0

b) 4000,0,0

c) 0,2000,2000

d) 4000,2000,2000

e) "Return"

Experiment with some more 3D Faces

Hints & Tips

1) You will notice the options .x , .y , .xy etc on the screen menu. These are point filters and they are very useful in 3D drawing. They permit you to split the entry of x,y,z coordinates into separate operations. For instance, selecting ".xy" would allow you to specify these two coordinates probably with the cursor on the screen then you will be asked for the z coordinate which can be typed in.

NOTES

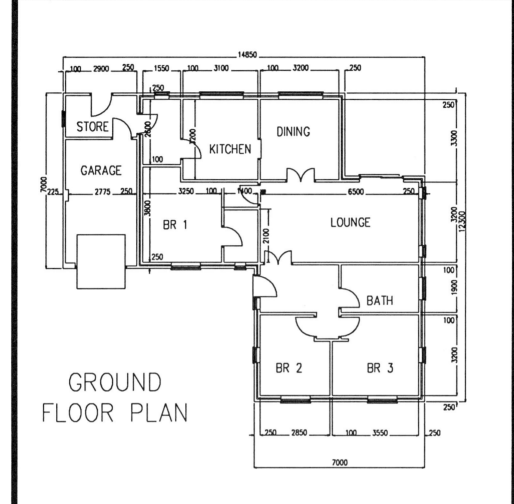

GROUND FLOOR PLAN

DRAWING HINTS :

This drawing is intended to be plotted at a scale of 1:50 so adjust your text size accordingly. You will need to set DIMSCALE and suppress the extension lines for internal dimensions (Dimvars DIMSE1 & DIMSE2). It is suggested that separate Layers are used for external walls, internal walls, windows & doors, dimensions and text.

DRAWING ASSIGNMENT No : 07

DATE COMPLETED : _____

STUDENT INITIALS : _____

THE AUTOCAD WORKBOOK

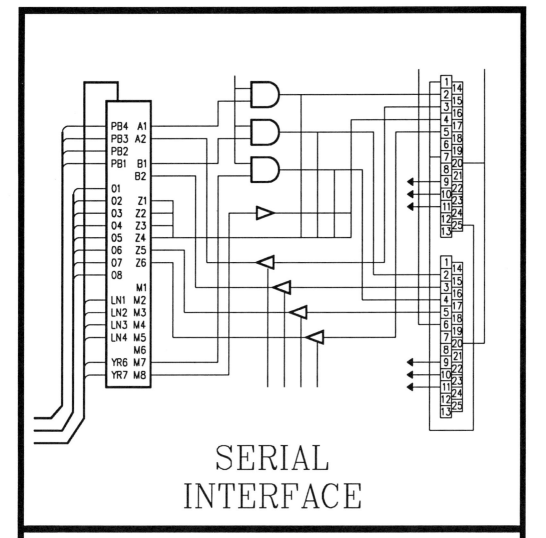

SERIAL
INTERFACE

SETTINGS INFORMATION :

This drawing was prepared using a 10 GRID and 5 SNAP. LIMITS
are (0,0) and (400,300). Components are in red, connections
in cyan and text in green.

DRAWING ASSIGNMENT No : 08
DATE COMPLETED : _____
STUDENT INITIALS : _____

THE AUTOCAD WORKBOOK

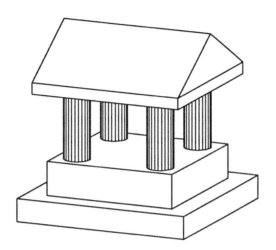

DRAWING HINTS :

The base consists of two squares with different ELEV & THICKNESS and the floors
are 3D FACES. The columns are circles (draw one, then use ARRAY). The roof
has a square topped by two sloping 3D FACES and the triangular gable ends
are also 3D FACES. Estimate suitable dimensions.

DRAWING ASSIGNMENT No : 09
DATE COMPLETED : _____
STUDENT INITIALS : _____

THE AUTOCAD WORKBOOK

11 : PLOTTING A DRAWING

PRE-REQUISITE KNOWLEDGE

Before starting this module you should be able to create an AutoCad drawing and to save it.

OBJECTIVES

After completing this module you should be able to:

1) Set up your plotter.

2) Specify what is to be plotted.

3) Assign the correct pens to be used.

4) Choose an appropriate scale for plotting.

5) Produce a pen plot.

6) Produce a printer plot.

INTRODUCTION

The ultimate aim of using a CAD system is to produce a drawing unless the drawing data is to be used to drive a manufacturing device directly. The plotting process can be problematical not because of any deficiency of AutoCad but usually because of the mechanical nature of the plotter itself. It is not uncommon for pens to dry up during a plot or the paper to become misaligned. There is no substitute for knowing your plotters foibles, using the correct pen/paper combination and keeping the plotter and pens clean and in good adjustment.

This module explains how to send a drawing to the plotter and will also mention obtaining plots with a dot matrix printer.

SETTING UP THE PLOTTER

It is impossible to be completely specific about setting up a plotter as there is such a wide variation in the types and sizes of plotters but the following is generally appropriate to the use of a pen plotter with multiple pens.

It is common that the plotter will be connected to the same port on the back of the computer as the mouse or digitiser i.e. the port with the dongle in it. So when you are about to plot, you should connect the plotter to this port.

Next switch the plotter on and it will usually run through a short test routine. You can now install the pens and paper. In order to get a good result the choice of correct pens and paper is critical. Below is a guide to the available combinations :

Ballpoint or Plastic Tip Pens - These are produced in many colours, are cheap and are disposable. They are best suited to plotting on ordinary paper and will produce the best results if the paper has a slight glaze. Too absorbent paper will cause the ink to "bleed" giving fuzzy lines. Typically they would be used for check plots to ensure that everything is how it should be.

Steel Tip Liquid Ink Pens - These are usually available in primary colours and different pen widths. They are often disposable and relatively modest in price (typically #5). They do not have a very long working life (typically 5 A1 size drawings) but this depends on the type of paper. They are suited to tracing paper and will wear rapidly on plastic film.

Tungsten Tip Liquid Ink Pens - These have the longest life and are generally refillable. They are relatively expensive (around #25) but in the long term may work out more economic than cheaper alternatives. They will produce excellent plots on tracing paper and plastic film.

As you install the pens in the plotter, ensure that they are clean, that the ink is flowing and make a note of the pen that you have placed in a particular numbered position of the pen holder.

Install the paper making sure that it is correctly aligned and that it is gripped securely.

You may now have to press some controls on the plotter to prepare it to receive the drawing data.

NOTES

SENDING A DRAWING TO THE PLOTTER

You should always save a drawing to disk before plotting it so that if things do go wrong you can always re-load the drawing.

AutoCad's PLOT command can be called whilst in the drawing to be plotted or can be selected from the Main Menu in which case you will have to specify the drawing name.

Before plotting ensure that you have frozen any layers that you do not want to appear and that the plotter is standing by.

On selecting PLOT, you will be prompted for what is to be plotted;

DISPLAY - Plots whatever is on the present screen display.

EXTENTS - Will plot all objects in a drawing regardless of the limits.

LIMITS - Plots to the declared limits of the drawing. Objects outside the limits will be omitted.

VIEW - will plot a pre-defined screen display.

WINDOW - asks for a window to be declared on the screen and all objects in this window will be plotted.

On selecting one of the above the text screen will clear and give a list of settings and ask if you wish to change any. This facility is useful if you are making a number of plots with identical settings in which case answer "NO". Otherwise answer "YES" and a whole series of prompts will begin :-

1) You will be asked for the number of the pen to be assigned to each colour. This is where your notes of which pen is in which numbered slot will be used. If you are using coloured pens and the red pen is in location 3 on the plotter, then you would reply "3" when asked for the pen for "red". Alternatively, if you are using different thickness of black pens with the 0.35 pen in number 2 and, on your drawing, you will have placed everything you want to appear in this thickness on a red layer, then you would reply with "2" for the pen for "red". When you have declared all the pens for the colours you have used, enter "x" and this section will have been completed.

On some plotters, you may also have been asked for linetypes. These are linetypes built into the plotter and you should always use "continuous" as AutoCad will supply the correct style. Trying to plot an AutoCad dashed line with the plotters dashed linetype can produce some interesting and unwanted effects.

2) Plot to file? - Some plotters are provided with their own software which will read files produced with this option. If you reply "YES" then you will be asked for a filename and AutoCad will convert its drawing into a form to be read by the plotter at a later date.

3) Size Units : Normally you would use "m" for metric. This does not affect the drawing in any way but just applies to the next prompts regarding paper size etc.

4) Plot Origin : If (0,0) is chosen then the plot will be placed with its bottom left corner in the bottom left corner of the paper. Using (50,30), for instance, would move the drawing along 50mm and up 30mm relative to the bottom left of the paper.

5) Plotting Size: You will be given a list of sizes that AutoCad knows are possible on your plotter and you can choose any of them or type in a special size if desired. This must be smaller than the largest size listed.

6) Rotate 2D Plots through 90 ? - This will turn the plotted drawing through 90 relative to its appearance on screen.

7) Pen Width ? - If you are filling in solid areas or have lots of wide Polylines, then you should enter the pen width that will be used to draw these features.

8) Adjust area fill boundaries for pen width ? - This refers to the answer to 7) above. If you had left the answer to 7) at 0.35 but actually had a 0.7 pen installed, then the pen would step across solid areas in 0.35 steps so overlapping its previous pass. This can result in excessive ink on the paper and will take longer.

9) Remove hidden lines ? - For plots of 3D drawings, if you respond with "YES" then the plot will resemble the effect produced by the HIDE command.

10) Plot scale - If you are using metric units then this option will mean " How many millimetres on the plot will equal how many drawing units on the drawing". If the drawing units were millimetres and you want a 1:50 scale plot, then enter 1=50. If the drawing units were metres and you want to plot at 1:2500 (say, for a map) then enter 1=2.5 .

Entering "F" means AutoCad will scale the plot to fit the available area.

If all is well, press "Return" in response to the next prompts and AutoCad will begin processing the drawing information into a form understood by the plotter and the plot will begin.

When the plot is finished, if you do not intend to do another right away, the pens should be removed and capped.

PRINTER PLOTS

The process of producing plots on a dot matrix printer is virtually the same as that described above for a pen plotter except, of course, there is no need to assign pens to colours. The command to start a printer plot is PRPLOT. The printer is connected to a different port on the computer so you do not have to disconnect the mouse or digitiser.

Printer plots are a quick, inexpensive method of examining the drawing and can reveal errors and omissions without wasting plotter paper and wearing out pens.

The plot origin is in the top left corner of the printer paper and the plot is produced on its side so the aspect ratio of the paper is the same as for normal A size drawings. There is no need to rotate the plots through 90.

NOTES

APPENDIX A: MS-DOS AND INSTALLING AUTOCAD

The first few sections of this module are some general information about the computer, its disk use and MS-DOS.

What does DOS do?

The PC family of computers have very few instructions built into them and the details of how the machine is to handle files, its disk drives and the peripherals which are connected to it are loaded in from floppy or hard disk when the computer is switched on.

Unlike, say, the BBC Model B or Sinclair Spectrum which have their operating system on a chip inside the machine, this loading the operating system from disk makes it very easy to use improved versions as they become available.The operating system used on the PC is MS-DOS (MicroSoft Disk Operating System) although you may find it called PC-DOS if purchased through IBM, and at the time of writing the latest version is numbered 3.40.

MS-DOS has a lot of code which is only intelligble to experts in this field but it also has a series of commands to allow you to carry out various operations usually concerned with copying files and similar matters.

What happens when you switch on ?

When the machine is switched on the following sequence of events takes place :-

1) The machine checks through its memory to make sure it is all working.

2) It then looks on Floppy drive A to see if the main MS-DOS file called COMMAND.COM is on a disk in this drive. On a hard disk machine this is not usually the case and drive A should be empty at this time.

3) It then looks on the hard disk, generally called Drive C, and COMMAND.COM should be there if the disk has been formatted (see below) in which case it will be loaded into the computer's memory.

4) Next it will look for a file called CONFIG.SYS if it exists. This file generally contains instructions related to the peripherals that are to be run.

5) Lastly, it looks for a file called AUTOEXEC.BAT which contains a number of DOS commands and executes the commands. The process ends with the DOS prompt appearing, namely C. Alternatively, AUTOEXEC.BAT may also load a program which could be a menu system e.g. Xtree, Gem etc or if the machine is dedicated to CAD, it can load AutoCad right away. If AUTOEXEC.BAT does not exist, you will go straight to the DOS prompt.

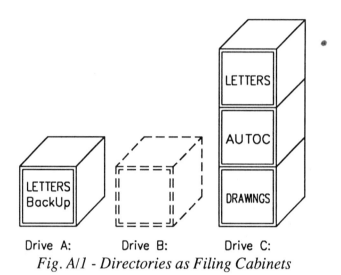

Drive A: Drive B: Drive C:

Fig. A/1 - Directories as Filing Cabinets

```
                    ┌──────────────┐
                    │     Root     │
                    │  Directory   │
                    │      \       │
                    └──────────────┘
                            │
        ┌───────────────────┼───────────────────┐
  ┌───────────┐       ┌───────────┐       ┌───────────┐
  │  LETTERS  │       │   AUTOC   │       │  DRAWINGS │
  │ Directory │       │ Directory │       │ Directory │
  └───────────┘       └───────────┘       └───────────┘
                                                │
                                        ┌───────┴───────┐
                                  ┌───────────┐  ┌───────────┐
                                  │ PROJECT 1 │  │ PROJECT 2 │
                                  └───────────┘  └───────────┘
```

Fig. A/2 - Typical Structure of a Hard Disk

What are directories ?

Every computer will be fitted with at least one, and generally more than one, disk drives. These are referred to by letters and a colon placed after the letter tells DOS that it is a disk drive. A common configuration is :

> Drive A: is the first floppy drive
>
> Drive B: is the second floppy drive (if fitted)
>
> Drive C: is the hard disk

These drives can be visualised as filing cabinets for storing information and all your drawings, word processor documents and programs (all referred to as files) are saved in these cabinets. Now, as with a conventional filing system, it is not sensible to just throw all files into a cabinet but you should divide the cabinet into drawers each of which holds a certain topic or type of file. With DOS, these drawers are called "directories" and you can also have sub-divisions of these directories called "sub- directories". With MS-DOS, the directory which contains all the files mentioned above is referred to as the Root Directory and all other directories are at "one level" below this in the so- called tree structure. This Root Directory does not have a directory name as such but is represented by the "\" character e.g. the Root Directory of the hard disk would be represented as C:\

Because floppy disks are of relatively small capacity and are cheap, it is not usual to bother to divide them into directories although it can be done if desired. You would normally use a different disk for each topic. However it is essential to divide a hard disk into directories so that information can be stored and recalled with the minimum of searching.

What does formatting do ?

When a brand new floppy or hard disk is to be used for the first time or you want to wipe an old disk clean, it has to be formatted. This process is like numbering the blank pages in a notebook before writing in entries. The computer will divide the disk into sectors and tracks so that it knows where it has stored data.

What are filenames ?

MS-DOS has rules about what files can be called and a filename will be of the form:

filename.ext

where filename consists of up to 8 letters and numerals and the extension is three letters that say what type of file it is e.g.

> HOUSE1.DWG might be drawing number 1 of a house.
>
> ACAD.EXE is the main program (i.e. EXEcutable) file of AutoCad.

What happens at the DOS prompt?

The prompt C> means the computer is logged on to drive C: and is waiting for instructions. You can then enter a DOS command.

MS-DOS Commands

This section is a brief summary of some commonly used DOS commands. There are some shortcuts ,not detailed here, which you will be able to use when you become confident about the usage.

1) To log on to another drive (in preparation to see what files are on it, for example) just enter the drive letter e.g.

A: - to log on to drive A

2) **MD < drive\directory >** : Makes a new Directory on the specified drive e.g.

MD C:\AUTOC - Makes a directory called AUTOC on drive C:

3) **CD < drive\directory >** - To Change to another Directory of the specified drive e.g.

CD C:\AUTOC - logs on to the directory AUTOC of drive C:

4) **DIR < drive\directory >** - will display a list of all the files on the specified drive\directory. If no drive\directory is specified, it will list the current directory.

The use of "wildcards" can be useful to limit the range of files displayed, in which the * symbol is used to represent any filename or extension e.g.

DIR C:\AUTOC*.DWG will list all drawing files in the directory AUTOC

N.B: the second \ character in this description is just to separate the directory and filename and should not be confused with the first \ which represents the Root Directory.

DIR C:\HOUSE.* will list all files with the filename HOUSE and any extension on the Root Directory.

If there are a lot of files to be listed, placing /W after the command will list them across the screen so displaying more e.g.

DIR C:\AUTOC/W

5) **COPY <source> <destination>** - copies a file from one place to another e.g.

COPY A:\MYBANK.LET C: - copies the file MYBANK.LET from the Root Directory of drive A: to the Root Directory of C:

COPY A:*.* C:\AUTOC - copies everything from the Root Directory of drive A: to the directory AUTOC of drive C:

6) **DEL <drive\directory\filename>** - Deletes the specified file e.g.

DEL C:\AUTOC\TRIAL.DWG - erases a the file TRIAL.DWG from the directory AUTOC of drive C:.

DEL C:\AUTOC*.DWG - deletes all files with the extension .DWG from the directory AUTOC.

Be careful using wildcards with the DEL command as you can easily wipe out something unforeseen.

7) **FORMAT -** will format a disk drive e.g.

FORMAT A: - will format a floppy disk in drive A:

Formatting a hard disk, though not too complicated is outside the scope of this book . Be warned, formatting a disk will erase all the information that is on it and the command to be avoided at all costs (unless you really mean it) is FORMAT C: which will wipe the hard disk.

8) **PROMPT** - Alters the display of the DOS prompt to show extra information. The most common form causes the prompt to show the current directory rather than just the drive letter e.g.

PROMPT PG - will display C:\AUTOC when this is the current directory rather than simply C. This command is often included in the AUTOEXEC.BAT file.

These are just a few of the commands which are used frequently and are especially useful for managing your draughting by making back-up copies or deleting superseded files.

Installing AutoCad

If you have followed most of the above then the sequence of installing AutoCad should be relatively straightforward. Assuming you have a formatted hard disk, then the procedure is as follows :-

1) Create a directory to hold AutoCad e.g. MD C:\AUTOC

2) Copy all the floppy disc files supplied with AutoCad to this directory e.g. repeatedly using COPY A:*.* C:\AUTOC

3) When all the disks have been copied, log on to the AutoCad directory e.g. CD C:\AUTOC

4) Make sure the dongle is installed in the back of the computer usually interposed between the computer and the mouse or digitiser

5) Load AutoCad for the first time by entering ACAD

6) A message will appear saying that AutoCad is not yet configured and you will be given lists of peripherals to choose from. Make sure you know exactly what type of screen you are using and the exact make of the mouse etc.

7) When you have finished this process, keep using the prompts to exit from the configuration stage.

8) Now AutoCad is ready to use.

9) If everything works you can exit from AutoCad and remove the large number of driver files used when configuring AutoCad e.g. DEL C:\AUTOC*.DRV

APPENDIX B - RELEASE 9

The new user of AutoCad would not find that the enhancements of Release 9 would be very significant with respect to Version 2.6 in the area of new commands or changed operation of existing commands. Most of the changes in this respect are only of importance to the experienced user. There is nothing in the AutoCad WorkBook that is incorrect when using Release 9 even though it is written for Version 2.6 .

The most significant change for the new user is the provision of the Advanced User Interface (AUI) and this will be of more interest to mouse users rather than digitiser users. The AUI provides a new way of selecting commands from pull-down menus. This can be used as an alternative to or in conjunction with the conventional AutoCad screen menu.

The tablet overlay is also slightly different, especially in the Display/Draw area where items have been re-arranged.

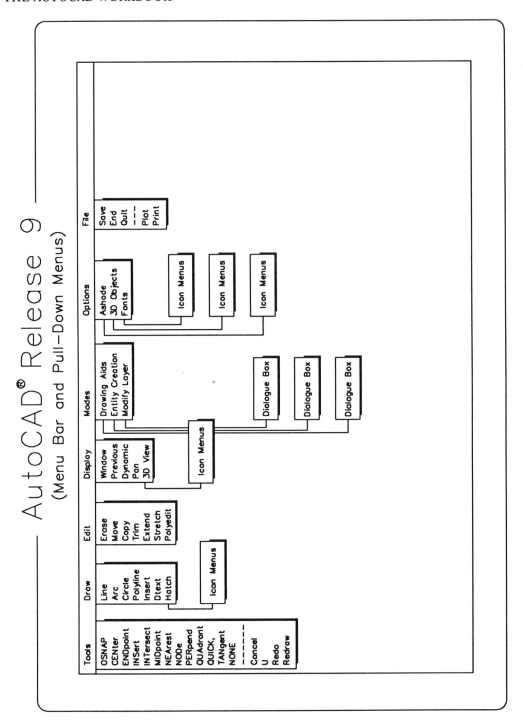

Fig. B/1 - AUI Menu Structure

ADVANCED USER INTERFACE

The AUI is similar in appearance and use to the GEM operating system and other WIMP (Windows, Icons, Mouse, Pull down menu) driven software. AutoCad's "baby brother", AutoSketch uses this approach as it is believed that users find it more intuitive.

One peculiarity of the implementation of this feature when AutoCad is installed in the usual manner is that the usual menu file ACAD.MNU only provides a few of the AutoCad commands in this form, however if you search the original floppy disks, you will find a sub-directory called "SOURCE" on one of them and in this directory is a file called ACADUK.MNU which contains virtually all the AutoCad commands in pull-down form. If you wish to use this then copy this file PLUS another called ACADUK.SLB to your AutoCad directory. When you have started a drawing, enter the command MENU and specify ACADUK as the menu name. This will then be active.

To use the AUI, you simply move the cursor to the region of the status line at the top of the screen and a series of headings will appear which roughly correspond to the headings of the Rootmenu. Clicking the "Pick" button on any heading will cause a window of AutoCad commands to appear from whch the desired command can be selected. You will notice that after the command has been used, it will repeat automatically as the writers of AutoCad assumed that it is common to work in this way. Selection of another command will cancel the repeat or entering "Ctrl" & "c" will halt the auto-repeat.

There are two other significant features of the AUI and these are the use of DIALOGUE boxes and ICON menus.

| Modify Layer | | | | | Up |
| | | | | | Page Up |

Current	Layer Name	On	Frozen	Colour	Linetype
✓	0	✓		White	Continuous
	Outline	✓		Red	Continuous
✓	Detail	✓		Blue	Dashed
	Label		✓	Cyan	Continuous

New Layer | | Page Down |
| | | Down |

OK   Cancel

Fig. B/2 - Dialogue Box for Layers

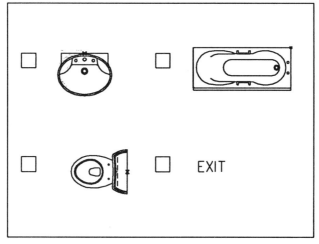

EXIT

Fig. B/3 - User Defined Icon Menu

DIALOGUE BOXES

These are used to improve the use of AutoCad commands which can require considerable typed input. Layer is a good example.

Exercise

> Select the heading "SETTINGS" then "LAYERS"

Now instead of having to enter "set" or "freeze" followed by the layer name, you can perform all these operations by highlighting the appropriate box and clicking the "Pick" button. To create a new layer simply click on the box at the bottom of the display and type in the new layer name.

Exercise

> Create some new layers and then assign different colours to them. Note that unless you have previously loaded various linetypes (with the LINETYPE command), you will not be able to use this feature to change linetypes on your layers.

ICON MENUS

This feature is similar to the Dialogue Boxes except that in place of the text in Dialogue Boxes you will be presented with a series of small pictures or Icons, each of which will have a small rectangle beside it. If you click the "Pick" button on this rectangle the feature illustrated by the icon will be implemented.

Exercise

> Select the heading "3D" and then "3D Objects".

You will see icons representing the various 3D objects you can draw. Unless you have set LISPHEAP and LISPSTACK to suitable values, these will not work so do not be surprised if you get the message "Insufficient Node Space" when you select one of them.

Exercise

> Investigate other headings and options of the AUI.

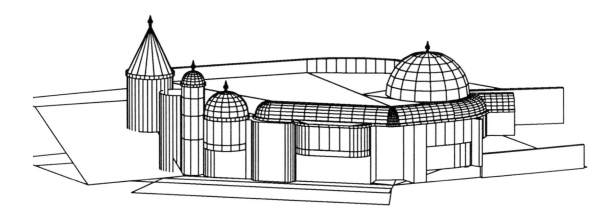

INDEX

A

Advanced User Interface   B/3
Arc   2/9
Area   8/11
Array: Polar   8/13
Array: Rectangular   8/13
AUI   B/3
AUTOEXEC.BAT File   A/1

B

Block: Command   7/3
Blocks: general   7/3
Break   4/9

C

CD: DOS Command   A/4
Change (Objects)   5/11
Circle   2/9
Colour   6/4
Computers   0/2
Coordinates   2/3
Copy   5/9
COPY: DOS Command   A/5

D

Dblist   8/7
DEL: DOS Command   A/5
Dialogue Boxes   B/5
Digitiser   0/7
Dim Command   9/3
Dim1 Command   9/3
Dimensioning   9/3
Dimvars   9/3
DIR: DOS Command   A/4
Directories (on Disk)   A/3
Disk Storage   0/3
Display Screens   0/2
Distance   8/11
Divide   8/15
Doughnut   4/7
Dtext   5/3

E

Elev   10/3
Ellipse   4/3
End   2/12
Erase   2/7
Extend   8/17

F

Filenames   A/3
Files Command   8/9
Fillet   4/11
FORMAT: DOS Command   A/5
Formatting (a Disk)   A/3
Function Keys   3/8

G

Graphics Screen   1/7
Grid   3/5

H

Hatch   8/3
Hatch: Patterns   8/5
Hide   10/7

I

Icon Menu   B/5
Insert   7/6

L

Layer: Color   6/4
Layer: Freeze   6/6
Layer: Make   6/3
Layer: New   6/2
Layer: Set   6/3
Limits   3/3
Linetype   6/5
Lispheap   1/3
Lispstack   1/3
List   8/7
Loading AutoCad   1/3

M

Main Menu 1/5
MD: DOS Command A/4
Measure 8/15
Mirror 5/9
Mouse 0/5
Move 5/9
MS-DOS A/1

O

Object Selection 2/7
Offset 4/11
Ortho 3/6
Osnap 3/7

P

Pedit 4/7
Pline 4/5
Plot Command 11/3
Plot Scale 11/4
Plotter Pens 11/2
Polygon 4/3
Polyline 4/5
Printer Plot 11/4
Prompt Line · 1/7
Prompt: DOS Command A/5
Prototype Drawings 3/6
Prplot Command 11/4

Q

Quit 2/12

R

Redraw 2/7
Rootmenu 1/9
Rotate 5/9

S

Save 2/12
Scale Command 8/15
Setup 3/2
Snap 3/5
Status 8/7
Status Line 1/7
Stretch 8/17
Style 5/7

T

Text Alignment 5/3
Text Command 5/5
Text Style 5/7
Thickness 10/3
Time 8/7
Trim 4/11
3D Face 10/9
3D Line 10/9

U

Units 3/4

V

Viewpoint 10/5
Vpoint: Axes 10/5

W

Wblock 7/7

Z

Zoom 2/11